Discovering the Outdoors

Discovering the Outdoors

A NATURE AND SCIENCE GUIDE TO INVESTIGATING
LIFE IN FIELDS, FORESTS, AND PONDS

Edited by
LAURENCE P. PRINGLE

PUBLISHED FOR THE AMERICAN MUSEUM OF NATURAL HISTORY
THE NATURAL HISTORY PRESS
GARDEN CITY, NEW YORK

ACKNOWLEDGMENTS

The editor's thanks to the authors of the articles that make up this book; to the editorial staff of *Nature and Science,* especially Franklyn K. Lauden; to the scientists of The American Museum of Natural History, who checked the articles for accuracy; to Joseph M. Sedacca, the designer of this book; and to the artists of the Graphic Arts Department, The American Museum of Natural History, who prepared the drawings.

The Natural History Press, publisher for The American Museum of Natural History, is a division of Doubleday & Company, Inc. The Press is directed by an editorial board made up of members of the staff of both the Museum and Doubleday. The Natural History Press has its editorial offices at The American Museum of Natural History, Central Park West at 79th Street, New York, New York 10024, and its business offices at 501 Franklin Avenue, Garden City, New York.

CONTENTS

ABOUT THIS BOOK

I grew up in a world of wooded hills and quiet ponds, where the sight, sound, or sign of a deer, hawk, or turtle was an everyday happening. Today, fewer and fewer people live so close to nature. I treasure those early years, especially because I now live and work in a big city.

Yet, I also look back on those years as a time of many missed opportunities. I roamed the countryside in all seasons, but I knew little about *how* really to explore nature. Where do you begin to look for the nest of a blue jay? How do you go about catching and studying the small mammals of a forest? What is known about the life in a pond? More important, what is not known?

Several years passed before I discovered the books that would have guided me in investigating the plants and animals around me. A book like this one would have helped.

The text of *Discovering the Outdoors* is made up of articles first published in *Nature and Science* magazine. Written by experienced biologists and naturalists, this book is an introduction to the plant and animal life you can find in nearby fields, forests, and ponds. It can be used to investigate nature almost anywhere outdoors—from a city park or weedy lot to a small suburban swamp or a great forest. Like *Nature and Science,* this book is a blend of information, questions you might try to answer, and helpful tips on how to go about answering them.

Most of the articles in this book are grouped into three kinds of living areas, or *habitats*—field, forest, and pond. (The life you find in a pond may also be found in a swamp, marsh, lake, or stream.) Before turning to the habitat that interests you most, read the chapter called "Getting Started." Besides telling how to keep good records of your observations, "Getting Started" will help you learn about the animal tracks and the birds found in many habitats.

In nature, different habitats and the life in them aren't as easily separated as they are in this book. You'll find fields and forests side-by-side. Turtles and snakes of different kinds live in several different habitats. In this book, however, you'll find snakes in "Exploring a Field," and turtles in "Exploring a Pond." The other plants and animals written about are grouped in the habitats where you are most likely to find them.

Discovering the Outdoors is an invitation for you to investigate the life that shares the earth with man. Just a century or two ago, a person without much training could still make important discoveries in such fields as physics, chemistry, and biology. Today, most fields of science are too advanced for amateurs. In biology, however, there are still opportunities for a "weekend scientist" to add to man's knowledge of life on this planet. Through careful investigations and patient observations, you may learn something new about the nest of a bird, the food of a snake, the ways of an ant.

Even if your discoveries are not new to science, this book will help you to understand better the wild plants and animals that are all around you.

LAURENCE P. PRINGLE

The American Museum of Natural History
January, 1969

6

Getting Started

Keeping a Field Journal

■Several years ago, I found the nest of a screech owl in a hollow tree. Recently I've been tempted to go back to the tree and take pictures, if owls still nest there. But where is the tree? I don't remember and didn't take any notes. The tree—and its owls—are lost to me forever.

You may have had the same thing happen to you. An event is fresh in your mind and you think that you'll never forget it. But months or years later you discover that you have forgotten important details.

To keep this from happening, you should keep a notebook (usually called a *journal*) just as many scientists do. As time goes by you'll find that the information "stored" in your journal becomes more and more valuable.

The journal itself doesn't have to be fancy. A loose-leaf notebook (about 6 by 9 inches) is best, and you should write your records in ink, not pencil. In one part of your journal you might keep notes that briefly describe the events on a hike or trip. Then on other pages you can keep more detailed notes on certain animals, plants, or other things that interest you (*see the samples on the next page*).

Here are some tips on the sort of information you should put in your journal to make your findings as accurate and valuable as possible.

DATE: When do migrating birds return to your neighborhood? About what time can you expect to find certain wild flowers in bloom? By keeping notes on these events—and recording the date—your journal will help you predict such events in the future.

TIME: The time of day when you see something also may be important. Animals are more active at some times than at others. You should also take notes on the timing of certain events. For example, how often does a robin bring food to its young? How often does your pet snake eat?

WEATHER: Just as your activities are affected by the weather, so are the activities of other animals and of plants. Keep notes on the temperature, clouds, rain, snow, wind conditions, and so on. With good records, you may be able to predict how certain animals and plants are affected by the weather. You might also try to predict the weather by observing changes in the kinds of clouds.

LOCATION: Don't overlook this "obvious" fact. Always record the state, county, and nearest city or town. "In the back yard" is not accurate enough, since you may move and might not be able to remember *which* back yard you meant. Even scientists sometimes find that they have not been specific enough about the location of something. When Charles Darwin was collecting finches in the Galapagos Islands, he just put the location "Galapagos Islands" on the birds' labels. Later he discovered that there were different kinds of finches on the different islands of the Galapagos group. From then on Darwin kept better records.

DESCRIPTION: Most people who keep journals regret that they didn't take more notes; they never feel that they've taken too many. What seems like an unimportant detail may be important later. You should jot down your notes as soon as possible after observing something. Use rough sketches, maps, or any other aid that will help you keep your notes accurate and complete. The samples shown on this page will help you get started ■

Laurence P. Pringle

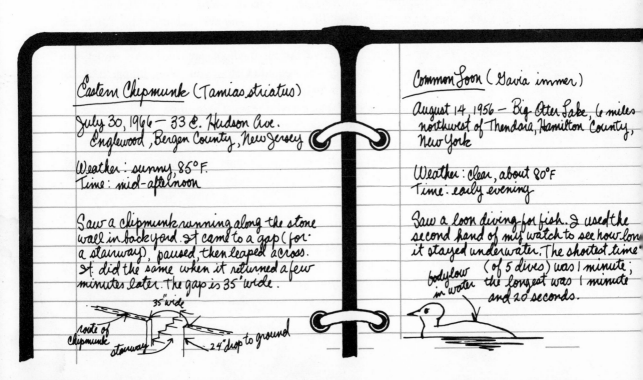

How to Be a Wildlife Detective

■You don't need to be a policeman to be a detective. You can get much the same thrill and adventure as a police investigator by becoming a wild-life "private-eye." Instead of tracking down criminals, you track animals. Instead of learning about robbers, you learn about wildlife.

Of course, the best way to study an animal's habits is to watch the creature. But that often is impossible. Many animals are active only after dark, and those that are active during daylight are too wary to let you near. If you are a detective, this shouldn't stop you. You simply look for clues that might reveal their habits.

The most useful kind of clues are tracks. These show up best in mud, sand, dusty roads, and in snow. You don't need to venture into the deep wilderness to find the tracks of wild animals. Within the limits of most big cities, you can discover tracks of such animals as rabbits, squirrels, mice, weasels, raccoons, and skunks.

Look at Your Own Tracks

You already know at least one track—your own. First chance you get, take a look at your barefoot print. How does it differ from the tracks of other animals? Right away you will notice that it is larger than almost any other track you will find. So you know that *size* can help you tell one

Can you solve this tracking mystery? The tracks in the photo are those of a musk-rat (in the center foreground) and a fox (at the left of the muskrat trail). The big footprints crossing the center of the photo were made by a man. The tracks reveal that the fox followed the muskrat, then attacked and killed it (leaving blood and signs of a scuffle in the snow).

kind of track from another.

Now compare your track with the track of a dog. You'll find at least three more important differences: (1) Your track is long, whereas a dog's is round. (2) The toes are all at the front of your track, but a dog's toes are on the front and side of the track. (3) A dog has only four toes. Remember differences in *shape,* for they will help you tell the tracks of one animal from another.

Before you can learn much more about tracks, you need some experience with different kinds. Winter is the best time to get this experience if you live in the northern states. (In areas without snow, you will have a harder time, but you can still study tracks in wet or dusty areas.) A day or two after a snowfall, go looking for fresh trails. Be sure to arm yourself—with a ruler or tape measure, a notebook, a pencil, and perhaps a camera.

How to Study Tracks

Fields, woods, vacant lots, and even your own back yard are good places to find tracks. Look around bushes, logs, trees, brush piles, and along fences or hedges. When you find a track, examine a single print. How long is it? How wide? How many toes does it have? Make a drawing of the print and jot down the measurements.

Then measure and sketch the spacing of the tracks. Is each print spaced

11

evenly in a trail? Or are there two, three, or four tracks bunched together? How far apart are the groups? If you have a camera, put your ruler near the tracks and take a picture of them. Jot down a note about where and when you photographed them.

Make the same sketches, measurements, pictures, and notes for each different kind of track you find. Then you can compare them with the drawings that begin on page 15, or with tracks shown in books (*see list on page 121*). You can best identify large tracks by looking at individual footprints. Smaller tracks can most easily be told by the pattern of their groupings.

When you recognize most of the tracks in your area, your detective work has just begun—and so has the fun. The next step is to follow a set of tracks. That is the way you learn about how an animal lives—how

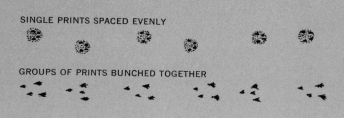

SINGLE PRINTS SPACED EVENLY

GROUPS OF PRINTS BUNCHED TOGETHER

it gets its food, what it eats, where it lives, how far it travels, and so on.

One very important rule to keep in mind when tracking is never to step on the tracks. You may have to examine them again. I learned this from a cottontail rabbit I once followed. After I had tracked it for several minutes, the track suddenly ended. I had almost decided that the rabbit had sprouted wings when I thought of another answer. Perhaps it had turned around and gone backward on its own track.

Upon looking at the rabbit's trail, I found it all scuffed out by mine. I couldn't tell whether or not it had backtracked. But by watching carefully along both our trails, I found where the rabbit had taken a long leap off to one side. Then it had continued on its way. As I kept on the trail, the rabbit pulled the same stunt six times. But I had learned, and was able to figure it out each time.

After you track an animal a little way, you may notice that its pace has changed. Try to figure out what the animal was doing. A good way to get clues about its pace is to study your own tracks again. First walk for several feet. Then hop. Then run at different speeds. Notice how different your tracks look each time. To imitate a rabbit or squirrel track, lean forward and put your hands into the snow. Then hop, using your hands for leverage and bringing your feet around in front of them. Remember

12

how the track looks, for it will help you tell which way a rabbit or squirrel track is headed. Usually their hind footprints are ahead of their front.

When tracking an animal, take notes on how far it travels, what kind of cover it uses (fields, woods, swamps), and what it eats. If you can follow it a long way, draw a map of its travels. Try to figure out why it goes where it does. If you find its den, note whether it is a hole in the ground, a hollow log, a tree, or what. Keep notes on where it is so you can come back and track the animal again.

This is exactly the method that scientists sometimes use to study animal habits. For instance, some biologists in Michigan have followed over two thousand miles of fox trails. They kept track of everything the foxes ate. Their results surprised many people, especially those who think that foxes eat mostly game animals, such as pheasants and rabbits. In one study, the

A RABBIT'S HIND FEET LAND AHEAD OF ITS FRONT FEET

foxes were trailed for 577 miles and killed only three pheasants in that distance. In another area they killed only five rabbits, two quail, and one hare in over one thousand miles. Both studies showed that mice, shrews, and *carrion* (dead animals) were the foxes' main food.

Solving a "Whodunnit"

Probably the peak of your detective career will come when you figure out a "Whodunnit"—a group of tracks where one animal chased, caught, and killed another. I saw such a set of tracks one spring. A fox had come upon a fresh muskrat track and followed it. Where the fox caught up to the muskrat there was blood and sign of a scuffle. Only one track left the area —the fox's.

There is much more to learn about tracking. With experience you will learn to tell an old track from a fresh one. You can learn to predict where certain animals will cross roads, streams, and valleys. But these things take experience, and there's only one way to get that. Go look for some tracks. And don't forget your notebook and pencil■   *Dave Mech*

Who Goes There?—A Guide to Animal Tracks

■The drawings on the following pages show the tracks and trails of sixteen animals that are common throughout most of the United States. Three are bird tracks; the rest are mammals. When you find an animal's track, take notes on its size, shape, the number of toes, and the pattern of footprints in the animal's trail. Then compare your observations with these drawings.

Remember that the size, shape, and clearness of tracks vary with snow or ground conditions. Tracks are distorted when snow thaws, and tracks made in fluffy snow or loose sand are not as clear as those shown here. The diagrams show both front and hind prints if they differ very much. Otherwise, just one print is shown. The captions tell the distances between footprints, or between sets (groups of all four prints) when the animal is walking or running■

Laurence P. Pringle

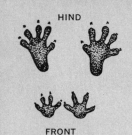

DEER MOUSE

Four-toed front prints are about ¼ inch long. Five-toed hind prints are about ½ inch long. Sets of prints are 3 to 6 inches apart when running. Tail sometimes leaves drag mark between prints.

HIND

FRONT

RUNNING

WALKING

GULL

Prints are about 3 inches long, and about 4 inches apart when walking. Webbed feet (for swimming) are similar to those of ducks, geese, and swans.

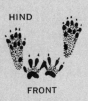

GRAY SQUIRREL

Four-toed front prints are about one inch long. Five-toed hind prints are 2 to 2½ inches long. Sets of prints are 20 to 24 inches apart when running.

HIND

FRONT

RUNNING

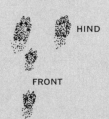

COTTONTAIL RABBIT

Claws and toe pads seldom show because of hairy feet. Front prints are about one inch long. Hind prints are 4 to 5 inches long. Sets of prints are 1 to 7 feet apart when running.

HIND

FRONT

RUNNING

LONG-TAILED WEASEL

Weasels have five toes on all feet but the fifth toe seldom shows in prints. Front prints are about an inch long. Hind prints are about 1½ inches long. Sets of prints are 12 to 22 inches apart when running, and hind prints often land in front footprints. Tail sometimes leaves drag mark.

FRONT

HIND

RUNNING

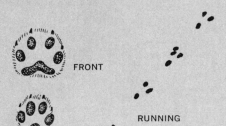

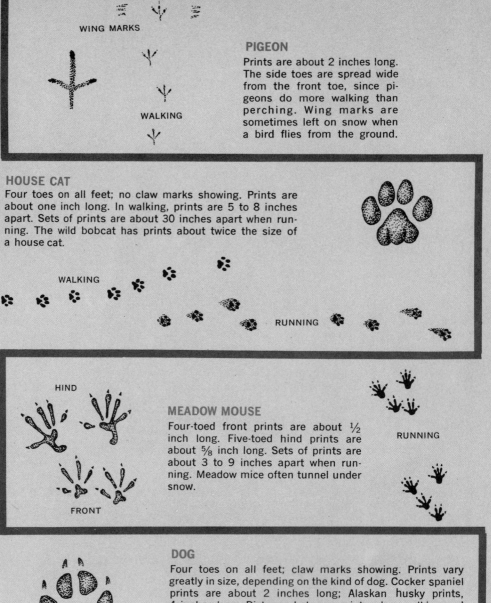

WING MARKS

WALKING

PIGEON

Prints are about 2 inches long. The side toes are spread wide from the front toe, since pigeons do more walking than perching. Wing marks are sometimes left on snow when a bird flies from the ground.

HOUSE CAT

Four toes on all feet; no claw marks showing. Prints are about one inch long. In walking, prints are 5 to 8 inches apart. Sets of prints are about 30 inches apart when running. The wild bobcat has prints about twice the size of a house cat.

WALKING

RUNNING

HIND

MEADOW MOUSE

Four-toed front prints are about $\frac{1}{2}$ inch long. Five-toed hind prints are about $\frac{5}{8}$ inch long. Sets of prints are about 3 to 9 inches apart when running. Meadow mice often tunnel under snow.

RUNNING

FRONT

DOG

Four toes on all feet; claw marks showing. Prints vary greatly in size, depending on the kind of dog. Cocker spaniel prints are about 2 inches long; Alaskan husky prints, 4 inches long. Distance between prints when walking and running also depends on dog's size.

WALKING

RUNNING

WHITE-TAILED DEER

Pointed prints are about $2\frac{3}{4}$ inches long. In walking, hind feet are often placed on top of front footprints. Deer can leap from 10 to 22 feet. Dewclaws, which are small unused "claws" behind the hoofs, sometimes show when foot sinks deeply into snow or mud.

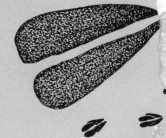

DEWCLAWS

RUNNING

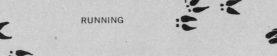

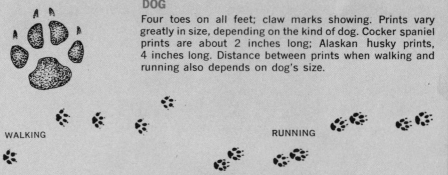

WALKING

SPARROW

Prints are about one inch long. Sparrows hop, leaving paired prints. Some other birds, such as crows, starlings, and pheasants, walk with prints in single file. Sparrows are perching birds; their side toes are not spread wide from the front toe.

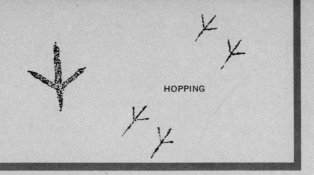

HOPPING

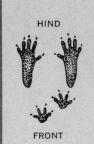

HIND

FRONT

RAT

Front prints are like four-fingered hands. Five-toed hind prints are about 1½ inches long and have long heels. Tail sometimes leaves a drag mark between prints. In walking, sets of prints are 3 to 4 inches apart. Sets of prints are 7 to 12 inches apart when running.

RUNNING

WALKING

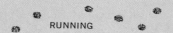

RUNNING

Four toes on all feet. Prints are 1½ to 2½ inches long. In walking, prints are in straight line, 12 to 18 inches apart. Sets of prints are 2 to 3 feet apart when running. Red fox has small toe pads; gray fox has larger, wider pads. Foxes have much hair on their feet, so toe pads may not leave marks.

GRAY FOX   **RED FOX**

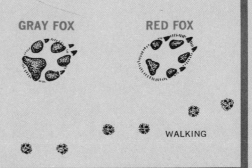

WALKING

FRONT

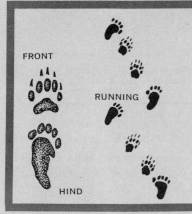

RUNNING

HIND

STRIPED SKUNK

Five toes on all feet. Front prints are 1 to 2 inches long and show claws clearly. Hind prints are 1½ to 2½ inches long and seldom show claws. Sets of prints are 6 to 12 inches apart when running.

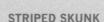

WALKING

RACCOON

Five toes on all feet. Front prints resemble hands and are 2 to 3 inches long. Hind prints are 3 to 4 inches long. In walking, sets of prints are 12 to 30 inches apart. Sets of prints are 2 to 3 feet apart when running.

FRONT

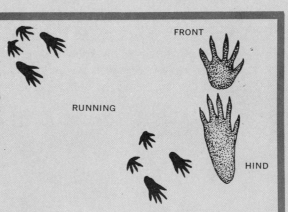

RUNNING

HIND

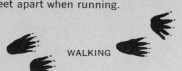

WALKING

How to Spy on Birds

■I am a bird watcher. Some people think that bird watchers are funny, and I don't blame them. Bird watchers do some odd things.

Sometimes we get up before dawn, put on old clothes, and hurry to the nearest swamp. Once in the swamp, we may sit for hours, or sneak around, peering into the bushes.

Bird watchers also seem odd to some people because of the names of the birds that we "watch." If you listen to bird watchers, you may hear, "There goes a yellow-bellied sapsucker!" Or, "Did you see that roseate spoonbill?"

Bird watchers admit that some birds have funny-sounding names. But many of the names *do* describe the bird—a yellow-bellied sapsucker is a woodpecker with a yellow belly. It pecks holes in trees and licks up the sap that seeps out. A roseate spoonbill is a rose-colored wading bird that strains food from swamps with its spoon-shaped bill.

There are about ten million bird watchers in the United States. Actually, many of these people do much more than *watch* birds. They *study* birds— taking censuses, learning about the mysteries of bird migration, and observing bird behavior. Bird study is a popular hobby because people are fascinated by the beauty, sounds, and movements of birds, and because there is so much unknown about birds.

Anyone who doubts that he can discover something new about a bird

18

should ask an *ornithologist* (a person who studies birds) about Mrs. Margaret Nice. Beginning in the 1930s, Mrs. Nice studied the song sparrows that lived near her home in Columbus, Ohio. She made all of her observations in her spare time while doing housework and raising five children. When her findings were published, ornithologists were amazed at the information she had gathered about song sparrows—their nests, eggs, territories, weights, movements, and so on. Even today, scientists use Mrs. Nice's research as a model for their own bird studies.

Learning to Identify Birds

Before you can study birds, you must be able to identify them. Autumn is a good time to begin. You can learn to recognize the birds that spend the winter in your area and then be ready to identify the many kinds that return in the spring.

You don't need much equipment: a field guide (*see list on page 12*), a pocket notebook, and a pen or pencil. Eventually you will want binoculars. However, they are expensive and you can get along without them for a while. I had over sixty birds on my "life list" (the total number of different kinds identified) before I bought binoculars.

Even if you live in a city, you probably know a few birds already. Knowing a few common birds helps to identify others, because you can compare the strange birds with those you know.

Here are some things to look for (and jot in your notebook) when you see an unfamiliar bird:

SIZE: How big is it? Compare it with birds that you know. Is it as big as a pigeon, or smaller than a sparrow?

SHAPE: Is its body long and slender, or short and chunky? Are its wings pointed or rounded? Is the bill long or short, thick or thin? Does the head have a crest? Is the tail long or short; rounded, square, or forked? Experts can identify many birds by their silhouettes alone.

MOVEMENTS: Does the bird fly straight or in a weaving, up-and-down pattern? Does it walk or hop?

HABITS: Is the bird climbing a tree, swimming and diving underwater, or soaring high in the sky? Does it flit about in the tops of trees, or stay near the ground?

MARKINGS, COLOR, and SONG: Does the bird have a plain, spotted, or streaked breast? Is there a stripe over its eye, or a ring around it? Is the bird red with black wings, or black with red shoulders? Is its song like the carol of a robin or the jeer of a blue jay? Surprisingly, these three characteristics are often not as important as others in bird identification. Some birds imitate the songs of others, and even experts can be fooled by tricky lighting that seems to change a bird's color.

A few years ago, two ornithologists spotted a strange bird in a New Jersey marsh. It seemed to have a green back and stripes on its throat. "A European species," they whispered, "or at least one from the North-

19

How many of these bird silhouettes can you identify by size and shape alone? Notice how the bodies, tails, and bills differ in shape. The birds are (1) grackle, (2) barn swallow, (3) chimney swift, (4) blue jay, (5) song sparrow, (6) robin, (7) meadowlark, and (8) crow.

west." With growing excitement they looked for some other markings. At last, they saw the bird clearly. It was a robin. The "green back" was imaginary.

One quick way to learn many birds is to go afield with an expert. There are probably several bird watchers in your area, and they may belong to a club which you can join. Many clubs have special censuses or "big days," when the members roam far and wide trying to find as many kinds of birds as possible in one day. These "big days" are usually held in early May, during the peak of spring migration, and near Christmas, to census the wintering birds.

Bird finding is much simpler if you know where to look. As you read about birds in field guides and other books, you will find many clues about their habits that will help you track down new kinds.

How to Study Birds

Some bird watchers are content to simply identify birds, trying to see as many as possible in a day, year, or lifetime. This is great sport—like hunting for trophies—and a test for your eyes, ears, and legs. However, bird watching can be much more than that. You can discover how birds live, and perhaps make a real contribution to science.

Begin with common birds that live in your own yard, garden, or along city streets. Each day, millions of people who live in cities see birds such as pigeons, starlings, and English sparrows. Yet, few of these people know how these birds live—their food, nests, territories, and so on.

Here are some questions you might try to answer about the birds in your area. Take the subject of migration. What kind of bird returns first in the spring? If you say, "the robin," many bird watchers will disagree. Try to find out this coming spring. Also, when birds return from the south, do both males and females arrive at the same time?

Keep notes on the arrival dates of different kinds of birds. Also note the weather. By keeping notes like these for a few years, you can predict when certain birds will arrive. You may also discover that some migrating birds are slowed by bad weather, but others are not. Try to figure out why. Might it have something to do with the kinds of food they eat?

There are many other parts of a bird's life for you to investigate—nest building, egg laying, the care and feeding of nestlings. You can easily spend all of your time studying just one pair of nesting birds. Or you might study all of the birds in one area, such as a nearby park or forest. Take a census of the birds in the area. Notice the numbers and kinds of birds that nest there. How do the birds' numbers change from season to season and from year to year? Try to figure out why bird numbers rise or drop.

By keeping careful notes on your observations, you may discover something new to science. You might even become an expert on the yellow-bellied sapsucker ■

Laurence P. Pringle

Luring Back Yard Birds

■Do nuthatches eat nuts? Do blue jays like the color blue? You can try to answer these and other questions about the ways of birds by feeding birds in your back yard.

Birds usually don't need to be fed to survive the winter. They do very well searching for such food as weed seeds and insect eggs, unless a blizzard or ice storm covers all of their natural food for several days. The best reason for feeding birds is to attract them so you can study them.

A feeder can be as simple or as complex, as costly or as inexpensive as you want it to be. You can buy bird feeders from garden stores and pet shops or make them from scrap lumber and other household items. The diagrams on the next page may give you an idea of the kind you would like, and the books listed on page 121 give detailed directions on how to build many kinds of feeders.

The kinds and numbers of birds that a feeder attracts depend on its location and the food offered. A feeder set in the middle of a lawn may not attract birds, because there is no nearby shelter for them. If you have no shrubs where birds can hide, drape or hang some pine boughs near the feeder for shelter.

To attract seed-eating birds, such as sparrows, cardinals, and juncos, offer seeds of sunflower, hemp, and millet, and grains such as corn and wheat. These are available from garden and seed stores. Insect-eating birds,

22

such as woodpeckers and chickadees, are attracted by peanut butter, suet, and fat trimmings (from a meat market). You can experiment with other kinds of food, such as fruit and table scraps. Begin putting out food in the autumn. Then the birds will discover the feeder and will begin using it as soon as winter arrives.

Some Things to Watch For

Take notes on what kinds of birds visit the feeder. When and how often do they visit? How long does a single bird or flock of birds stay at one time? Note the weather and see how it affects bird feeding.

Try to discover where else the birds roam in your neighborhood. What is the size of their winter territory? Is it bigger or smaller than their summer territory? Why?

You can learn a lot about bird behavior at a feeder. Do the birds feed one at a time, or in groups? How close will a bird allow another bird to get to it? Do some kinds of birds chase others away from the food? Do birds eat at the feeder or carry food away? What do birds do while waiting to get to the feeder?

Color some sunflower seeds with food coloring. Then put equal numbers of the different colors and of normal seeds in the feeder. Do the birds avoid any particular color? If so, can you figure out why?■

Laurence P. Pringle

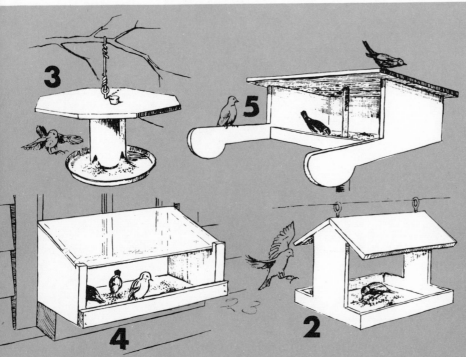

You can build or buy bird feeders like these. Hanging feeders (1, 2, 3) help protect birds from their enemies. Make a suet stick (1) by drilling holes in a piece of wood and filling the holes with suet. A window feeder (4) allows you to study birds at close range. A weathervane feeder (5) keeps its back turned toward the wind.

23

Exploring a Field

The Life in a Field

■A biologist named Frank Lutz once wrote a book called *A Lot of Insects,* based entirely on the insects that visited the city lot where he lived. Exploring such a field can be a fascinating hobby.

If you live in a city, you can explore a vacant lot. If you live in the suburbs, in a small town, or in the country, you will probably have a greater choice of fields to explore. The important thing is to pick one, then visit it often to see what is going on.

Try to pick a field that has a variety of plant life in it, including some shrubs and tall weeds. The more varied the plants, the more varied the animals that live with the plants. (You might check this idea yourself by comparing the insect life in different fields, some with a great variety of plants, others with mostly one kind of plant.)

Begin with a Map

A field is the home of a community of plants and animals. One of the goals of your visits to a field can be to discover what kinds of plants and animals live there and how they fit into the community. At first glance, a field may look lifeless. You may see some birds or butterflies flying over, but nothing much seems to be happening in the field itself. Move into the field, however, and you will begin to discover the complex community that

25

lives there.

On your first trip to a field, just walk around and explore the whole area. You should keep notes on your observations. Make a rough map of the field, marking landmarks such as an outcrop of rock or a hedgerow boundary. Pace off the edges of the field so that you can draw your map to scale (such as one inch on the map equals one hundred feet on the field).

On later trips, you can concentrate on a particular part of the field that interests you, or on certain plants or animals. The other parts of this chapter may give you some ideas of things you can observe.

From Field to Forest

"Change." Keep this word in mind as you explore a field. A field is always changing, although the changes may be too slow to be seen in one visit. Over the summer, however, you may see some changes and also find clues about past and future changes in the field.

You may have seen a lawn, garden, or farmer's cropland that became a weed-grown field when it was abandoned. This is how most weedy fields begin—as bare soil or a planted field. On the prairies of the central United States, abandoned farmland changes into grassy fields and stays that way. There isn't enough water for trees to grow, except along streams or ponds. In most other parts of the country, however, a field is just an early stage in a long series of changes that lead to a forest. Here is how it happens:

FROM FIELD TO FOREST

Beginning with bare soil on the left, this drawing shows how a field slowly changes from open land to a forest. As the plant life changes, so does the animal life. This drawing shows plants and animals that might be found in fields of the northeastern United States; you may find a different succession of plants and animals in your area.

The first plants that grow on an abandoned patch of soil are usually those called *annuals,* which live for just one growing season. They include peppergrass, ragweed, and other kinds of plants that thrive in open, sunny spots. But as the years pass, the annual plants lose their places to others, such as mullein, Queen Anne's lace, and many kinds of grasses. These plants live more than one year and they don't need open, sunny places in which to get started. They crowd out the pioneer plants.

After a few more years the grasses and tall weeds must compete for sunlight, water, and other needs with other plants that spring up—berry bushes, shrubs, quick-growing trees like sumac, and tree seedlings. If the field is undisturbed by man, eventually the trees become so big that their shade keeps many of the smaller plants from getting enough sunlight for life. A forest grows where there was once an open, grassy field.

Since these changes take many years, you can't observe them in one field in one summer. But you can probably find some signs of the past and future stages. You may still be able to find parts of a field in the

early, annual weed stage. And, while most of the field is filled with grasses and tall weeds, you may find some tree seedlings that will someday grow large and be part of a forest.

See if you can find long-lived weeds that are crowding out the annual kinds. If you find any young trees, notice if their shade has affected the kinds of plants beneath them.

As the plant life of a field slowly changes, the animal life is also affected. Meadow mice thrive among thick grasses and weeds. When the grasses become sparse, meadow mice can't survive. They may be replaced by deer mice. Meadow larks and killdeer feed and nest in open fields. Later, when taller plants take over, these birds no longer find ideal living conditions. Birds such as song sparrows, catbirds, and cardinals live among the shrubs and saplings.

Be sure to record your observations in a notebook. There is still much to be learned about the changes of plant life in an area (called *plant succession*). You might discover something important. Also try to take some photographs of the field as it is today. Keep the photos (and negatives) with your notes. Years from now you can revisit the field and see for yourself how it has changed ■

Laurence P. Pringle

Meadow mice (1) are common in grassy, weedy fields. They are seldom seen because they are active mostly at night. When the plant life of a field changes to mostly shrubs and trees, mice such as the white-footed or deer mouse (2) become common.

WHERE DO THE SEEDS COME FROM?

Many of the pioneer plants that spring up in an abandoned field grow from seeds that are carried by the wind. But many seeds are too heavy to be spread by the wind. As you find different kinds of plants growing in a field, try to find out how their seeds got there. How could an oak acorn or berry seed reach the middle of an open field?

1

2

These photos show some of the animals you may find living in fields. The garter snake (2) may even be found living in vacant lots of cities. Woodchucks (5) are wary rodents that live on farms, along roads, and in suburban fields. You may find meadowlarks (3) in the same sort of fields where woodchucks live. Killdeer (4) nest and feed in fields that have little or no plant growth, while moles (1) can be found in underground burrows in many kinds of fields, including lawns.

3

HOW VACANT IS A VACANT LOT?

If you live in a city and have no park or other open country nearby, make a survey of the different kinds of plants and animals living in a vacant lot. What sort of plants grow there? What kinds of animals either live in the lot or visit there? Dig into the soil and look for earthworms, sow bugs, and other small animals. By making several visits during the summer (especially at different times of the day), you may discover a surprising amount of life in the midst of the city.

EXPLORE AT NIGHT

Some of the animals living in a field are active only at night. To explore the field at night, take along a flashlight and insect repellent. Move slowly and quietly, listening to the night sounds. Try to find night-calling insects and identify them. Are any flying insects attracted to your light? See if you can find insects and other animals by reflections of your light from their eyes. Also look for the wary small mammals, such as shrews and meadow mice, that live in fields.

LAYERS OF LIFE

In a forest, certain animals live mostly high in trees, others live in lower trees and shrubs, and still others spend most of their lives on the ground. Find out if there are similar "layers of life" in a field. Watch to see if there are any birds, insects, or spiders that spend most of their time near the tops of plant stems. Do other kinds of animals live mostly on or near the ground?

LITTLE CLIMATES

The animals living in a field don't have the same climate as you do when you walk through a field. For one thing, the air close to the ground contains more water vapor than the air above the plants. The plants give off this water vapor from their leaves.

You might try to find other ways to compare the climate near the base of the grassy jungle with the climate at the tops of the weeds. Make two identical pinwheels (see *diagram*). Put one close to the ground among the plants and the other at the height of the tallest weeds. Compare their spinning on a breezy day. Also use a thermometer to find the temperature at ground level and at weed-top level. How does the weedy growth affect the temperature near the ground?

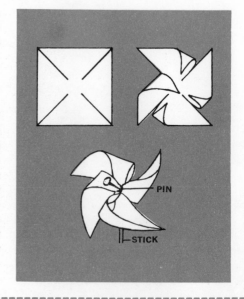

A Plant and Its "Partners"

■It is not surprising to find an animal that depends on plants for its food. But you can sometimes find certain animals that depend on *a particular kind* of plant for life. You can have some fun with these special plants by watching to see how many different kinds of animals live on or in them.

A good plant to observe is *milkweed*. You can find this tall plant (2 to 5 feet high) growing in fields, meadows, and along roads almost everywhere in North America. Once you locate a milkweed patch, you can begin to study the life in, on, and around the plants.

Pay special attention to the flowers. They attract many insects. Their colors and strong odors lure butterflies, moths, bees, and other flying insects. As an insect crawls among the flowers after nectar, one of its legs may get caught in a tiny slit in a flower. If the insect is small, it may be stuck there and die. You may see some of these. Larger insects, however, usually pull free. When they do this, they break away a part of the flower that contains grains of pollen. Then, when the insect flies to another milkweed flower, it carries the pollen along.

Inside the pollen are male sex cells. In the milkweed flower the- male sex cells *fertilize* egg cells. Milkweed seeds then develop from the fertilized egg cells.

Of all the milkweed insects, the best known is the monarch butterfly. This bright orange and black butterfly lays its eggs on the underside of

33

milkweed leaves. After three or four days, a tiny caterpillar (*larva*) emerges from the egg and begins to feed on the leaves. Later the caterpillar leaves the plant and develops into a *chrysalis,* from which the adult butterfly eventually hatches.

The monarch is not the only milkweed insect with bright colors. You may find beetles and bugs with orange and black markings. Now the monarch isn't eaten by birds and other animals; its bright color seems to be a warning that it doesn't taste good. Is the same true of the bright-colored beetles and bugs? No one knows.

The milky juice of milkweed plants contains chemicals that can be poisonous to mammals, birds, and other animals. Is it these chemicals that make monarchs bad-tasting? Again, no one knows.

Not all insects living on milkweeds are brightly-colored. Green aphids suck juices from the plant. (Whether chemicals in the juices affect the taste of aphids is not known.) Midges lay their eggs inside milkweed stems and leaves, and their larvae develop there. Wasps visit milkweed plants regularly, not to feed on the plant, but to catch some of the other insects there.

Still other animals probably eat milkweed seeds. The seeds develop in a pod that breaks open in the fall, gradually releasing hundreds of small seeds that have fluffy parachutes. While the seeds are still attached to the pod, you can watch to see if any birds, mice, insects, or other animals feed on them. Once the seeds break free from their pods, the wind carries them away.

The milkweed is just one kind of field plant that has different kinds of insects, spiders, and other animals depending on it. You might try observing other kinds of plants, such as goldenrod and thistle. Whatever plant you pick, try to find a growth of it close to where you live. Then you can visit it frequently, increasing your chances of discovering new things about the plant and its animal life ■

Laurence P. Pringle

The Ways of Weeds

■There are no weeds in nature!

In nature there are different kinds of plants and animals, but no one kind (*species*) is of any greater value than any other. "Value" and "importance" are terms used by humans and have meaning only to us.

What, then, are weeds? Weeds are plants that we don't want to grow in places where we *do* want other plants to grow. We don't *cultivate* weeds, or plant and water them, as we do grass or plants in a flower or vegetable garden. Yet the weedy plant often grows exactly where we don't want it—on the lawn or among our cultivated plants.

Not only do weeds grow where they are not wanted, but they usually succeed in growing *better* than the species cultivated by man. Weeds are among the most vigorous species of plants. They can survive a drought that kills cultivated plants, and they thrive in open places with plenty of sunlight. This means that the farmer, with his open sunlit fields, finds weeds one of his greatest headaches.

The seeds of most weedy plants are long-lived. The seeds of mullein, for example, can sprout after eighty years and probably longer. Weeds also grow faster and taller than cultivated species, which are soon blocked from direct sunlight. It is no wonder that the gardener, farmer, or lawn-keeper dislikes them.

36

Why Weeds Succeed

The common kinds of weed do not belong to any one family of plants; just about every major group of flowering plants contains weed species. However, many common weeds belong to the families of flowering plants that have evolved most recently, such as the grasses, mints, and composites (which include daisies, asters, and sunflowers). Members of these plant families can grow well in places where the conditions—of soil, moisture, and so on—are quite different. They produce many seeds and have ways of scattering the seeds far and wide.

Weeds also have a number of ways of spreading without seeds. Some weeds, for example, produce a *rhizome*—an underground, horizontal stem. The rhizome grows rapidly and sends up aerial shoots as it grows.

There are weed trees, shrubs, and herbs. Many weeds are *perennials;* they live for many years, and each year shed seeds. Many other weeds are *biennials,* which live for two years. During the first year they produce

This weed is growing in poor soil, surrounded by concrete, in air containing automobile fumes. Like all weeds, it can survive where other kinds of plants would die.

roots, stems, leaves, and during the second year they send up flowering stems and produce seeds. A number of other weeds are *annuals,* which live for one year. These plants grow from seeds, flower, produce seeds, and scatter them—all in the short space of one growing season.

Well over half of our common weeds were not growing in North America when the first colonists arrived from Europe. The early settlers brought weeds to America, sometimes on purpose, sometimes by accident. Weeds arrived from Europe in the ballast (such as rocks or gravel) that was used as weight in the holds of colonial ships. Some weed seeds probably arrived among the seeds of crop plants brought from Europe.

As the forests fell before the colonial ax, as roads were cut through the wilderness and the prairie schooner traveled them, and as the roadbeds for railways spread across America, weed plants soon sprang up in these open, sunny areas. Weeds marched across the land hard upon the colonists' heels ■

Lawrence J. Crockett

The "Unwanted" Plants

■How many different kinds of weeds can you find in your neighborhood? Weeds grow everywhere you go—from city sidewalks to country roadsides. The drawings on the following pages will help you recognize ten of the most common weeds in North America; the captions tell something about the lives of these plants and why they are so successful■

Lawrence J. Crockett

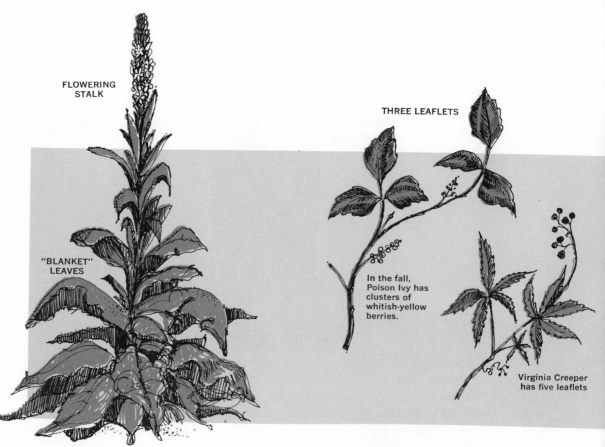

FLOWERING STALK

"BLANKET" LEAVES

THREE LEAFLETS

In the fall, Poison Ivy has clusters of whitish-yellow berries.

Virginia Creeper has five leaflets

GREAT MULLEIN

Great mullein is also called, and for good reason, "blanket leaf." Its large leaves are covered with many branched hairs, which make them look whitish and fuzzy and feel velvety to the touch. Blanket leaf is often seen along roadways or in vacant lots. It must have sunlight. In its second year, this plant has a long flower-bearing stem. The stem is covered with bright yellow flowers which first open three quarters of the way up the stem. The last flowers to open are at the top of the stem, which may reach a height of 10 feet.

POISON IVY

This plant is poisonous to touch. To some people it is poisonous even to be near. Poison ivy is a vine with leaves that grow on alternate sides of its stem. Each leaf is made up of three shiny leaflets, toothed along their edges. The shiny material is the poisonous chemical urushiol, which causes painful blistering of the skin. Do not confuse this dangerous plant with the harmless and attractive vine called Virginia creeper. Its leaves are not shiny and each has *five* leaflets.

WILD CARROT OR QUEEN ANNE'S LACE

The leaves of this biennial look lacy or feathery (much more feathery than those of the common ragweed). The great number of tiny white flowers in little clusters (called *umbels)* form a large cluster that looks like lace. At the center of this large flower cluster (four or five inches across) you can find a single black or purple flower. Crush a leaf and notice the pungent and somewhat unpleasant odor. Other members of the carrot family also produce strong odors. After this plant's flowers have produced seeds, each tiny flower bends inward on its stalk, giving the whole flower cluster the appearance of a bird's nest. This accounts for the third common name for this weed, bird's nest weed.

CRABGRASS

Crabgrass is a European plant and is the curse of the lawnkeeper. Its leaves and leaf-stem sheaths are very hairy. Appearing on the lawn in midsummer, it quickly sends out horizontal stems *(rhizomes)* which grow along the surface of the ground, producing leaves and rooting rapidly. The spreading rhizomes shade out the grass beneath. By the time this lawn invader dies with the first frost it has killed your grass and left ample seed to give you more trouble next year.

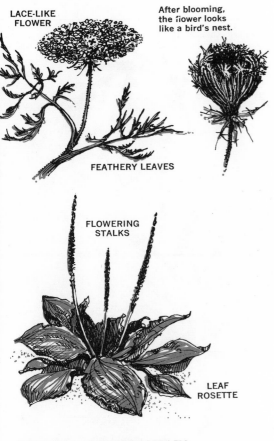

LACE-LIKE FLOWER

After blooming, the flower looks like a bird's nest.

FEATHERY LEAVES

FLOWERING STALKS

LEAF ROSETTE

FLOWER CLUSTERS

SPREADING RHIZOME

FLOWERING STEMS

BROAD-LEAVED PLANTAIN

This common weed of poorly kept lawns has a tap root topped with a *rosette* (circle) of large rounded leaves with easily seen, depressed veins. The tiny, pinkish flowers grow on long, thin stalks, from their tops to about one inch above the ground. The circle of leaves shades out grass beneath. Each of the many flowers produces many seeds, helping to spread this weed far and wide. The broad-leaved plantain came with colonists from Europe.

CANADIAN GOLDENROD

The goldenrods do not cause hay fever! Their pollen is sticky and is spread by insects, not carried by air to the nose of the hay fever sufferer. This particular goldenrod (there are hundreds of species) grows three to six feet tall. It has narrow, lance-shaped leaves which are smooth above and downy beneath. The golden flower clusters grow along a stem that is held at right angles to the main stem. Goldenrods thrive in sunny, open fields that are not cultivated.

ENGLISH PLANTAIN OR RIB GRASS

This plantain also has a rosette of leaves but each leaf is much thinner than those of its cousin. The thin, dark green leaves are deeply veined (hence the name rib grass). Its 6-to-10-inch long flowering stalks end in stubby clusters of flowers. When the pollen-producing stamens are mature they look like pins stuck in a cushion *(see diagram)*. Rib grass is a vigorous seed producer and a threat to a handsome lawn.

COMMON RAGWEED

Common ragweed is the giant ragweed's cousin and one of the most common of all weeds. It may grow to be five feet tall, and has leaves that are only two to five inches long, but it produces much more pollen than its taller cousin and is a great nuisance to hay fever sufferers. The leaves of this ragweed are easily told from those of the giant ragweed; they have a lacy or feathery appearance. Both ragweeds bloom from July to October. Both produce many seeds.

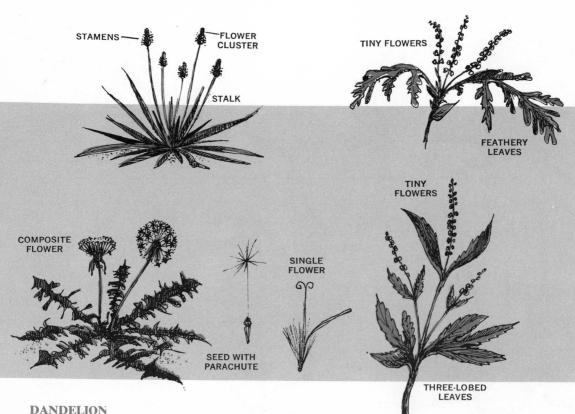

STAMENS — FLOWER CLUSTER
STALK
TINY FLOWERS
FEATHERY LEAVES
COMPOSITE FLOWER
SINGLE FLOWER
SEED WITH PARACHUTE
TINY FLOWERS
THREE-LOBED LEAVES

DANDELION

The dandelion's rosette of leaves is made up of many deeply-lobed leaves. They are edible when young, and can be cooked or used in salads. The thin, hollow, pale green stalks are topped by dense clusters of flowers. The cluster is so dense that it seems to be a single flower. Pick a dandelion and pull it apart. How many individual flowers do you find? Each is an entire flower. (A "flower" composed of many individual flowers is called a *composite*.) Usually each of these tiny flowers produces a seed, which is attached to a delicate parachute that helps the wind carry the seed away from the parent plant. A single dandelion plant blooms from May to October, producing thousands of seeds.

GIANT RAGWEED

This annual plant may grow 15 feet high! Its rough-hairy leaves have three to five lobes. You may find leaves a foot long on the taller plants. Ragweed's tiny, greenish flowers grow on special stems near and at the top of the plant. The male flowers shed great amounts of pollen that is carried away by the wind. It is this pollen that is one of the main causes of hay fever.

Insects of the Grassy Jungles

■At first glance, you may not see any life in a vacant lot or field. By getting down on your hands and knees and looking among the plants, however, you'll find lots of life. You'll find death too, for the many insects and other small animals living in fields can be divided into two groups— the hunted and the hunters. You may actually see one kind of insect hunting and killing another.

To study the lives of common field insects, you need a hand lens (or magnifying glass), a notebook and pen, some empty jars, and a trowel. You should also have a book to help you identify insects (*see list on page 122*).

I can suggest some of the insects to look for, but what you find is going to depend on where you live and the type of plants growing in your neighborhood. Wherever you live, I'm sure there will be insects eating the plants and other insects eating those insects.

Introduction to the Plant Eaters

To get to know the plant eaters, look for damage to leaves. On some leaves you will find blotches or winding lines. If you hold one of these leaves up to the light you may see a wormlike larva tunneling its way through the leaf. This is a leaf miner. It spends its larval life between

CABBAGE BUTTERFLY

PRAYING MANTIS

APHIDS

LADYBIRD
BEETLE

GRASSHOPPER

GROUND
BEETLE

EARWIG

ANT

SOWBUG
(NOT AN INSECT)

42

WIREWORM

the top and bottom surface of the leaf—a rather narrow home!

There are many leaf miners. Some are the larvae of moths and some of flies. If you find a leaf with a pupa (usually inside a small "blister"), put the leaf in a jar until an adult insect emerges from the pupa. Use a magnifying glass or hand lens to see the moth or fly that comes out; they are mostly very small.

Also, look for the sapsuckers. The commonest of these are aphids. Sapsuckers have mouth parts that pierce the leaves to suck the sap. This injures the leaves. The feeding of aphids causes many changes in a plant, such as rolled or blotched leaves.

Dig into the soil and you may find some of the root feeders. The wireworms are among the most destructive. They are larvae that develop into

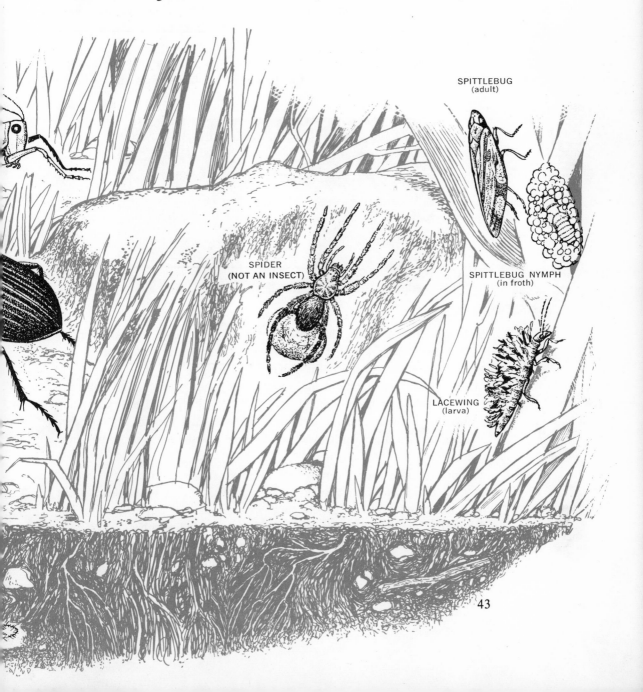

SPITTLEBUG
(adult)

SPIDER
(NOT AN INSECT)

SPITTLEBUG NYMPH
(in froth)

LACEWING
(larva)

43

click beetles. Most of the root feeders are the larvae of beetles and flies.

You may find many other kinds of plant-eating insects, including grasshoppers. Watch especially for spittlebugs which often live on grasses and alfalfa. The young (called *nymphs*) produce a froth from their bodies that completely surrounds them. This froth seems to protect the insects from their enemies and also provides the moist environment they need for life. (Take a spittlebug from its froth and set it on a grass stem. Then see how long it takes for the insect to produce a new "house" of froth.)

The Hunters

The insect eaters, or *predators,* are often fast runners with alert senses. An example is the ground beetle. It has long legs, long antennae, large eyes, and big powerful jaws. As you'd guess from its name, it is a ground dweller and eats soil insects.

A good way to get to know the ground beetles is by setting *pitfall* traps. These are just jars sunk into the ground. The beetle falls in and can't

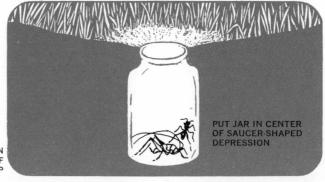

CROSS SECTION
VIEW OF
PITFALL TRAP

PUT JAR IN CENTER
OF SAUCER-SHAPED
DEPRESSION

climb out. Be sure that the rims of the jars are level with, or below, the surface of the ground. If you can set the jars in the middle of saucer-shaped depressions so much the better.

Using nothing more than a half dozen empty jars, you can find out a lot about the habits of insect ground predators. Put the jars in different kinds of areas—in a lawn, under a tree, in tall weeds, in a garden. I found that the busiest place in my garden was beside some boards that were rotting in a corner.

Empty the jars each morning and evening, and keep a separate record for each jar. From your results can you find one area where beetles are most abundant? Would you say they are more active during the day or night? How are they affected by the temperature and weather?

Besides beetles, you will catch other kinds of insects (such as ants and earwigs) and animals such as spiders and sow bugs (*which are not insects*). Sow bugs and earwigs are not predators but are *scavengers*—garbage dis-

44

posals.

An easily recognized beetle you may see is the ladybird or ladybug beetle. These insects aren't swift, long-legged creatures like the ground beetles. They live almost entirely on aphids, which are easy to catch and eat. Ladybug eggs are sometimes laid in the middle of a promising aphid colony. When the young hatch they find a meal waiting for them.

Another aphid eater is the lacewing, a delicate, pale-green insect with large, transparent wings. The larvae of some species carry debris on their

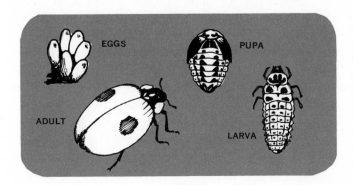

Ladybird beetles and many other insects go through these four stages of development during their lives. Other kinds of insects, such as grasshoppers and spittlebugs, have just three stages — egg, nymph, and adult.

backs as a kind of camouflage. The debris is made up mostly of skins of its victims. If you find one of these lacewing larvae (*see diagram on page 43*), carefully strip off the debris and you will see there are rows of hooked bristles on the body segments to hold the covering. Put the larva and the debris in a small jar and watch to see how it replaces the pieces.

The hover fly also lays its eggs in aphid colonies. The larva, a sluglike creature, sucks out the inside of the aphid, leaving only the dry skin.

It sounds as if the aphids have a bad time of it. But aphids reproduce at a tremendous rate. Someone has figured that, starting with one female, there could result *822 tons* of aphids in eighteen weeks! This shows why we need predators such as ladybirds, lacewings, and hover flies.

How Much Does a Ladybird Eat?

There are some investigations you can do to find out just how helpful these predators are. For example, you can try to find out how many aphids a ladybird will eat in a day. Put a ladybird in a small jar or bottle and put in a little moist paper towel to keep the air humid. Then take a leaf and use a fine brush to knock off all but ten aphids. Put the leaf with its aphids in the jar. Next day, take out the leaf and see how many aphids have been eaten. (Be careful not to count any shed skins as dead aphids.) Then put in a fresh leaf with ten more aphids. If your ladybird always eats all ten aphids, try offering more.

You can also try feeding the larvae of ladybirds. One thing to notice is that a larva that is about to shed its skin stops eating for a while. This happens, too, before it forms a pupa. Look for a very young larva—or better still, eggs—and see if you can find out how many aphids a ladybird beetle eats during its larval stages.

Another experiment you can try is to find out what happens to a larva that gets barely enough to eat. When you know how many aphids a larva will eat, then you can figure out a starvation diet. Will this result in an undersized adult, or will it just take a longer time to produce a regular sized adult?

When working with aphids you are sure to come across some dead, but not shriveled, aphids. They are usually light brown and are stuck to the leaf. These have been attacked by *parasites* and are called *mummies*. The parasites are small wasps and you may see them running and flying near the aphids. If you are very lucky, you may see the wasp stick its long *ovipositor* into an aphid to lay an egg. The aphid is the food supply for the wasp that develops from the egg. Take a close look at the aphid mummy. If there is a small hole in it, the parasite has emerged. If there is no hole, put the aphid mummy in a jar and watch for the tiny wasp to come out. Like the predators, the parasites help control the number of plant feeders.

When doing these investigations, keep asking yourself questions; then try to find ways to answer them. (Remember that to be sure of your answer you should repeat an experiment or observation several times.) Even in a small field or lot, there are enough insects, spiders, and other small animals to study all year long ■

Margaret J. Anderson

Aphids suck sap from many kinds of plants. The adults are about a quarter of an inch long, or less. Try to find out how many aphids can be eaten in one day by a ladybird beetle.

A Snake for a Pet

■Have you ever had a snake as a pet? If you have, you are already one of many people who find these unusual animals fascinating to watch and study. If you haven't, perhaps you are curious about them and would like to keep one for a while.

The number of snakes living near towns and cities has been greatly reduced because their natural living areas have been destroyed or disturbed. But some species such as the common garter snake in eastern North America and the plains garter snake in the Midwest may be common in back yards and in vacant lots. They even turn up in small vacant lots in the largest cities. If you search carefully you may find some snakes near your home or in a nearby park.

Snakes are often hard to find even when they are plentiful. The small secretive kinds often live almost under the very noses of people. I recently discovered over thirty-five small DeKay's snakes under flat boards and old newspapers in a vacant lot in New York City. I found them in a space 12 feet long by 7 feet wide. Later I asked people living nearby if they had ever seen a snake. They said that they had, but only in a zoo.

Where to Find Snakes

Some of what might seem to be the most unlikely places to look for

47

snakes are often the best. Good places to investigate include vacant lots with rubbish, stone walls and fence rows, and abandoned fields. In these areas there are places for snakes to hide and good sources of food. The best place to begin your search is under flat objects resting on the surface of the ground, such as boards, flat stones, and logs.

A garden cultivator with three metal *tines,* or prongs, is a useful tool to use in turning over boards and logs. Always replace the shelter in its original position after lifting it so that animals in the area may use it again.

Many experienced snake collectors make a sort of "snake trap" by plac-

A
SNAKE
CAGE

SCREENED HOLES
FOR AIR TO
PASS THROUGH

METAL
HOLDERS

FRONT OF GLASS
OR SCREENING

WOOD

To hold a snake properly, support the weight of its body in your hands and do not squeeze it tightly.

48

SNAKE	FOOD
garter and ribbon snakes	small frogs, salamanders, small fish, tadpoles, and earthworms
DeKay's snake or brown snake	earthworms, slugs
water snakes	fish, frogs, tadpoles
black snakes, corn snakes, bull snakes, rat snakes	mice, other small rodents, occasional small birds
king snakes, indigo snakes	mice, other rodents, other snakes
green snakes	crickets, grasshoppers, other insects

ing flat objects in open fields or other places where snakes might live. You might try this too. Visit the board or other object each day to see if snakes have found shelter underneath.

Before you begin your collecting, be sure to check a field guide on snakes. You should be able to recognize the two main groups of poisonous snakes found within the United States. Snakes in the "pit viper" group include the rattlesnakes, copperheads, and water moccasins. Two kinds of coral snake make up the second group. *Under no conditions should you try to catch or keep a poisonous snake.* It is not only dangerous but it is against the law in many places to keep a poisonous snake in your home.

However, try not to confuse harmless snakes with poisonous ones. Harmless water snakes are often mistaken for the poisonous water moccasin that is found in southern states, northward to southern Illinois. A good rule is never to collect a snake unless you definitely know that it is not dangerous.

Catching Snakes and Caring for Them

The best way to catch snakes is with your hands. Since harmless snakes (nonpoisonous) may bite when first captured, you should wear a pair of leather gloves. After a few days in captivity, most snakes get used to being handled and even seem to enjoy being picked up.

The most important piece of equipment you will need is a few cloth bags in which to carry your catch. Flour and sugar sacks are good for this purpose but first be sure they have no holes. You can also use pillowcases. Air passes freely through these bags, so the snakes can breathe inside. A string sewed at one end can be used to tie the end when closed.

Before catching a snake, you should have a proper home ready for it.

49

Many questions about snakes remain unanswered. Through your study you may be able to discover some important information about the lives of snakes. Here are some things you can observe and take notes on:
- When and how often does your snake shed its skin?
- What type of food does it eat?
- How often does it feed? How much does it eat at one time?
- Keep records on its growth and weight over a period of time. How fast does it grow?
- Describe any courtship behavior you see. Does the snake lay eggs or produce living young? What is the size and number of eggs laid? What is the size and number of living young produced? How long does the egg tooth stay on the snout of a young snake after it escapes from its eggshell?
- Is there anything unusual about your snake—its color, its body structure, its habits?
- Under what conditions did you find your snake? When you find a snake, keep notes on the date, place, time of day, weather, and other conditions.

You can make a cage or cages from many different materials. One easy way to make a cage is to get a screen top for an old aquarium tank. Before placing your snake in its cage, check to make sure that the container is free of cracks and that the lid is securely fastened to the cage.

Put some fine sand or gravel with a few small rocks or twigs on the floor of the cage. In most cases it is best to keep the inside of the cage dry at all times. Snakes may get skin diseases if the cage floor is kept wet. Since snakes drink water, put a small open dish in a corner of the cage and keep it filled.

Many scientists regard snakes as among the cleanest animals in the world. To help them keep clean in a confined cage, be sure to remove any wastes that accumulate.

Snakes may die within ten or fifteen minutes if forced to remain in the direct rays of the sun. For this reason, keep your cage in a place where it won't get much direct sunlight.

Many species of snakes feed on only one kind of food. They refuse to eat anything else. When you capture a snake, find out from a field guide (*some are listed on page 122*) what kind of food the snake usually eats before you try to feed it. The hog-nosed snake or puff adder usually feeds only on toads. The common garter snake usually eats such food as earthworms, small frogs, salamanders, tadpoles, and small fish. Sometimes a pet garter snake will even eat bits of raw chopped meat (*unseasoned*) when this food is moved slowly in front of its head, or better, mixed with earthworms.

If you take good care of your snake, it will thrive and you can learn a lot about the ways of snakes. If you have trouble finding food for your pet, however, take it back to the place where you found it and let it go ■

Kenneth Bobrowsky

Exploring a Forest

Life of the Forest Floor

■The forest floor is a spongy carpet. Except for a scurrying chipmunk and some wild flowers, it may look still and dead. Just the opposite is true. There is more life and activity here than in any other part of the forest. Here is where the forest blends with the earth. Here is the tree nursery —where forest life starts. And here is where life in the forest ends.

The floor of a forest is a fascinating place to explore. This chapter tells about some things you can look for when you visit a woods, either in the country or in a city park. Let's begin with the beginning—a tree seed.

Once a tree seed is mature, it falls to the forest floor. If conditions are right, the seed will sprout and grow into a tree. Most seeds are not ready to grow when they first reach the forest floor. Some have tough, waterproof coatings. It takes almost a year for moisture to work through these seed coats. Other seeds must be chilled for a time before they begin to grow. Certain seeds with hard, protective coats begin to grow after they have gone through the digestive systems of birds or mammals.

From their nursery on the forest floor, seeds become sprouts, then seedlings, saplings, and finally trees. But only a few of the thousands of seeds that fall ever become trees. Many seeds are eaten by mice, insects, and other animals. The seedlings are also eaten by animals. And each young tree competes with other plants for sunlight, water, and minerals from the soil.

The Forest Wastebasket

Foresters estimate that about four thousand pounds of plant and animal material fall upon an acre of forest floor each year. Dead or wind-blown trees make up only part of this debris. Leaves, tree flowers, fruits, seeds, twigs, plants such as wild flowers, and dead animals are all included in the total. Everything that lives in the forest eventually becomes a part of the litter.

Yet the forest does not become choked in its wastes. Each leaf, twig, or tree that falls is chemically broken down by many kinds of plants and animals. This is why there is more life and activity in the litter than anyplace else in the forest. Stick your hands into a soft part of the forest floor. In one pound of this material you may hold up to thirty billion soil bacteria—the tiny living things that break down some of the plant and animal wastes.

There are also many soil animals in the forest. The ones that are most abundant are too small to be seen without a microscope, but there are also many you can see. A few years ago, scientists dug up a square foot of forest floor, one inch deep, in a New York forest. They could see 1356 living animals, mostly insects and mites.

You already know of some bigger animals, such as toads and chipmunks, that live on and under the forest floor. But dozens of other kinds of animals are not as noticeable. Shrews dart through the litter searching for food. Deer mice make their homes in hollow logs. These small mammals are usually active at night and are seldom seen.

Layers of Life and Death

Most of the fascinating world of the forest floor remains hidden from view. To explore it takes a little digging. Use a small trowel to dig through the litter. Have some pill bottles or other small containers in which to store specimens for later study. To collect microscopic animals, take home a couple of handfuls of the forest floor in a plastic bag. Keep it as near to its natural condition as possible—moist but not soaked in water. Then take tiny bits of decayed leaves, put them on a glass slide, add a drop of water, and look at them with a microscope. The diagrams on page 56 show some of the tiny organisms you may see.

After scratching away the top layer (last year's leaves and twigs), you will find parts of leaves or leaf skeletons. These will be fragile and fairly well decayed. The first wave of the woodland "waste disposal system" has already been at work. This is carried out mostly by bacteria and fungi which are most active during warm weather. They do not need sunlight, as most other plants do, and can "work" around the clock. As a leaf or twig is broken into ever finer pieces, more of its surface is exposed to decay. As you dig deeper, you probably won't be able to tell where decayed leaves end and where soil begins. The leaves and other material have

DADDY LONGLEGS

EARTHWORM

Countless animals and plants live—and die—in the few inches of litter that cover the forest floor.

decayed into rich, dark *humus*—the top layer of soil.

You will find many kinds of animals in the humus and in the layers of rotting leaves. Take along a hand lens (small magnifying glass) to get a close look at them. Mites and springtails will be most common. You should be able to find dozens or even hundreds of them. Springtails are well named for they turn backflips when exposed to the air.

You may also find millipedes, earthworms, rove beetles, sow bugs, mole crickets, daddy longlegs, spiders, and many others. About 95 per cent of all insects spend one or more stages of their lives in the soil. When you add these to all the other animals that crawl and burrow in the soil, you can understand why the forest floor feels like a soft carpet when you walk on it. It is punched full of holes. There are tunnels, channels, burrows, passageways—millions and millions of them.

54

This drawing shows a few of the animals you may find among the mosses, rootlets, humus, and decaying leaves.

With each bit of digging in the litter, the rich, life-giving humus is mixed with soil particles. This mixing and digging also helps give the forest floor its blotterlike ability to hold water. The holes and tunnels serve as miniature water reservoirs, holding the rain or melted snow until it has time to soak deep into the soil. The leafy litter and humus are spongy, and hold still more water. By soaking up rainfall, the forest floor keeps the water from wearing away the soil and helps prevent floods.

The Worms' Turn

As you explore the forest floor, you will probably find some earthworms. They are especially valuable animals in the forest. When earthworms take leaf fragments into their slitlike "mouths," bits of soil from the worms' burrows are taken in with the leaves. As the material passes through the worms' bodies, it is broken down and ground up until it is like a paste. Finally the remains of the digested leaves are deposited on the surface as

ROUNDWORM
(magnified 30 times)

PARAMECIUM
(magnified 180 times)

ROTIFER
(magnified 100 times)

In the water-filled spaces of leaf fragments, you'll find many microscopic animals like these.

tiny pellets, called *castings*. You may have seen these little mounds in gardens and lawns.

In their simple ways, earthworms are important forest animals. Through their burrows, air and water enter the forest soils. Through their feeding, leaves and other plant materials are digested and mixed with the soil. Then the minerals and other "building blocks" of the leaves can be used again—perhaps by being taken up by the roots of a tree or wild flower.

Earthworms can't do the whole job by themselves. They cannot digest wood, for instance. Also oak leaves and pine needles apparently have so much acid in them that earthworms cannot digest them. Earthworms are not abundant under oak and pine trees.

It takes the combined activity of earthworms, insects, mites, fungi, bacteria, and many other plants and animals to keep the forest-floor "factory" working. When you get down on your knees and study the forest floor, you will see how it all fits together. There will be seeds, tiny plants, and countless hidden animals. Waste products of the forest will be present, slowly being changed to be used again. It is a silent world of death and rebirth, and a fascinating world to explore ■   *Rod Cochran*

----- INVESTIGATION -----

Collect a square foot of forest floor, one inch deep, put it in a plastic bag and take it home. Go through it and try to find and identify as many animals as you can. Then make a "Berlese separator" to catch the animals you missed. The diagram on this page shows how to make one and the labels tell how it works.

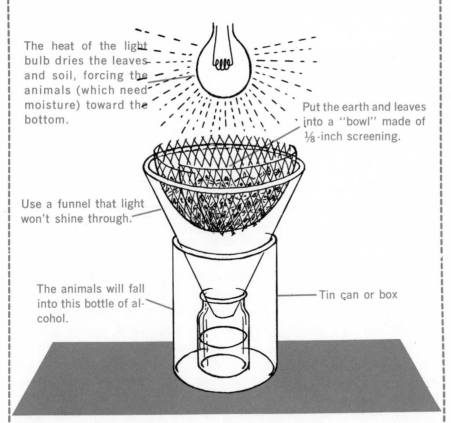

The heat of the light bulb dries the leaves and soil, forcing the animals (which need moisture) toward the bottom.

Put the earth and leaves into a "bowl" made of ⅛-inch screening.

Use a funnel that light won't shine through.

The animals will fall into this bottle of alcohol.

Tin can or box

After a few days, take out the alcohol bottle and pour its contents into a white saucer. You will probably need a magnifying glass to identify your catch. What is the total number of animals you found in your small chunk of forest floor? Do you think you would find different numbers and kinds of animals in other parts of a forest? In other seasons? Try to find out. The book list on page 122 will help you identify the animals you find.

Fungus Fruit

■In summer or early fall, take a walk through a woods two or three days after a soaking rain. Look for the many kinds of mushrooms that have sprung from decaying logs or the forest floor. You will be amazed at their different colors and shapes. There are over a thousand kinds (*species*) of mushrooms in North America. They all belong to the group of plants called *fungi.*

Unlike wild flowers, colonies of mushrooms are not destroyed by picking. You may gather all you want. This is because it is impossible to remove the *mycelium,* or network of many tiny threads from which mushrooms grow. The mycelium grows underground and may extend ten feet or more from the mushrooms. As long as the mycelium finds food in rotting wood or leaves, it will continue to grow and produce more mushrooms. (The mushrooms are the fruit of the fungus plant. They produce the spores from which new fungi grow.)

Unfortunately, though mushrooms grow very rapidly, they break down even more quickly. They may shrivel away, or be devoured by insects, or simply decay into a slimy blob.

One way to become better acquainted with these plants is to collect and preserve them for future study. For gathering the mushrooms, all you need is a basket, a small gardener's trowel or a dull knife, some waxed paper or plastic bags, and a pencil and pad of paper for taking notes.

Collecting and Drying

Use the trowel or knife to lift the mushrooms from the soil so their lower parts won't break off. Then put each mushroom or group of mushrooms in a plastic bag, or wrap them in waxed paper, twisting the ends of the paper tightly to keep the mushrooms moist and clean. Take notes on each group of specimens. Note when and where you found them, their color when fresh, and their odor. Later, you should put this information on labels for the different specimens.

You may also want to make "spore prints" from the mushrooms. The diagrams on this page show how. Spore prints will help you identify the mushrooms you find.

To dry your mushrooms, get some *silica gel* crystals from the houseware department of a department store, or from a hardware store. (Silica

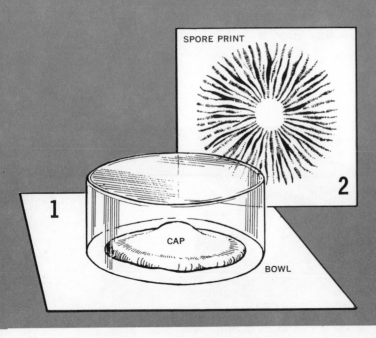

MAKING A SPORE PRINT

SPORE PRINT

1

2

CAP

BOWL

1. Put the mushroom's cap, bottom down, on a sheet of white paper. Cover the cap with a glass bowl and leave it undisturbed for several hours.

2. The tiny spores fall on the paper and stick, forming a beautiful and colorful pattern. The color of the spores is a clue to the identification of the mushroom.

gel crystals soak up moisture and are used to dry damp places, like closets. The coarse 14-20 mesh size is fine for sticky or big fungi. The fine 28-200 mesh size is best for fragile or small fungi.) The crystals can be used over and over again.

You can dry the mushrooms in plastic containers or large coffee cans with airtight lids. First put a layer of silica gel crystals on the bottom of the container. Then arrange some mushrooms on it. Be sure that the specimens do not touch each other. Pour more crystals around and over the mushrooms. Then cover the can tightly and let it stand until the specimens are crisp and dry—usually after a day or two. Pour off the crystals carefully. Pick out the specimens with a pair of tweezers and place them (with their labels) in boxes for storage. Use a soft brush to remove any crystals still clinging to the mushrooms. Finally, put some naphthalene flakes or moth balls in the boxes to repel insects that might damage your specimens.

Some Mushroom Mysteries

Collecting mushrooms is a fascinating hobby. You can quickly learn to identify groups of mushrooms by using a field guide (*see book list on page 122*). Later you'll be able to recognize individual species. You may find some rare ones. By the way, it takes careful study to tell edible mushrooms from poisonous kinds. *Never eat any mushrooms you find unless your identification has been checked by an expert.*

This summer, see what you can discover about the mushrooms that grow in your area. How many different species are there? Do some species grow only on rotten wood? What kinds of animals eat mushrooms?

Mushrooms grow very quickly. Do you think you could figure out a way to discover just how fast they grow? ■

Florence Hoseney

The place where you find a mushroom can be a clue to its identity. Some kinds grow only in wet evergreen forests. Others grow only on decaying logs or stumps.

Weather in the Woods

■Some sunny day in the summer, take a few minutes and walk from a hot "desert" to a cool "mountain." You will find the desertlike conditions at the surface of a sidewalk, driveway, or parking lot. To find cool "mountain" weather, simply go to the nearest woods.

The trees that make up a forest have a remarkable effect on its *climate* (the weather an area has over the years). For example, you will find that most of the sunlight that beats down on a sidewalk never reaches the ground in a forest.

One sunny July afternoon, a forester measured the amount of sunlight at different levels in a New Jersey woods. He found that some sunlight was reflected from the tops of the trees. More than half of the sunlight was soaked up by the leaves of the treetops (*canopy*). Only about one fifteenth of the sunlight reached the small trees (the *understory*). In some parts of the woods, less than one hundredth of the sunlight reached the forest floor.

The forester discovered that the amount of sunlight at different levels in the forest also affects the temperature of the air. At the top of the canopy, the temperature was 96° Fahrenheit. At the forest floor it was 71°.

Trees have other effects on a forest's weather. Strong winds that whip across open fields are slowed to a light breeze inside a forest. Rain beats down on open land, loosening soil and sometimes washing it away. In a woods, the rain from a brief shower may not even reach the soil. Many drops cling to leaves, twigs, and bark. Some of these drops drip gently to the understory and finally to the forest floor. A few drops soak into the rotting leaves. A lot of rain must fall before the water begins to reach the soil beneath the spongy, decaying leaves.

The investigations tell how you can study some of the ways the trees of a forest affect its weather from day to day and from season to season ■

Laurence P. Pringle

INVESTIGATIONS

• Make two rain gauges, like the one shown on the next page, to measure the amount of rain that falls in a storm. When you have made the two rain gauges, set one on the ground in an open field and the other inside a woods. After a rainstorm, measure the amount of rain that fell in each. How much rain was kept from reaching the gauge by the shrubs and trees of the forest? Measure the rainfall of several storms, including light showers. Can you figure out how much rain must fall on a forest before water begins to collect in the forest rain gauge?

• A forester discovered some differences in temperature in a woods on a sunny day. Would you expect the same conditions on a cloudy day? To find out, get at least four inexpensive thermometers. Make sure that they are all working correctly (set them in one place for a while and see if they all have the same reading). Then set the thermometers in different places in and near a woods. Put one on the forest floor. Put another underneath the layers of rotten leaves. Tie or tape another to a dead sapling (at least ten feet long) and lean the sapling against a tree (this will give you the temperature of the air at that level). Put the fourth thermometer on the ground in an open field near the woods.

Take notes on the temperatures at these different places on a sunny day. Then see what the temperatures are on a cloudy day. Is there a bigger difference in temperatures at the various places on a sunny day or on a cloudy day?

How to Make a Rain Gauge

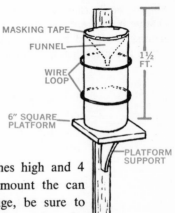

RAIN GAUGE

MASKING TAPE

FUNNEL

1½ FT.

WIRE LOOP

6" SQUARE PLATFORM

PLATFORM SUPPORT

WOOD SUPPORT 4 FT. LONG

■You will need one large fruit juice can about 8 or 9 inches high and 4 to 5 inches in diameter. Remove the top of the can and mount the can firmly, as shown in the diagram. When you use your gauge, be sure to place it out in the open in a well-exposed area, not up against a shed. To prevent the gauge from being blown over, loop rings of clothes-hanger wire around the post and collecting can. You can fasten the wire to the post with heavy staples. The wire loops should be just snug enough so that you can remove the can easily.

If it rains during the night, some of the water you have collected will evaporate before you make a measurement in the morning. You can stop a lot of evaporation by fitting a funnel into the can (*see diagram*). The top of the funnel must be the same diameter as the top of the can. In a hardware store you can buy a funnel made of soft plastic and cut a little bit of the rim off so that the funnel fits the can snugly. To keep the funnel from slipping into the can, or from being blown away, tape the edge of the funnel to the can with strips of masking tape. This completes the rain gauge, but now you need a measuring jar.

You'll have to get a tall, slender, straight glass or jar with a flat bottom, like an olive jar. The container must be no more than 1 or 1½ inches wide to give an accurate measurement of the amount of rain that fell.

Remove the plastic funnel and pour *exactly* one inch of water into your

63

When a windy rainstorm rages at the top of a forest, the weather is different near the forest floor. The wind (shown by arrows) is slowed by leaves and branches. Rain clings to leaves and drips gently to the ground.

rain gauge can. Now pour the water into the slender container. With fingernail polish and one bristle of a paintbrush, mark a very thin line on the container at the watermark. This mark shows one inch of rainfall. Now mark off ten equally spaced units from the bottom of the container to the one-inch mark. Label the top mark "1 in."

If you wish, you can mark your measuring container to a depth of two inches. Just pour two inches of water in your collecting can and go through the measuring steps again.

Put the rain gauge outdoors and wait for the first rainfall. Then remove the gauge from its wooden base, pour the water into the measuring glass, and read off the amount of rainfall to the nearest tenth of an inch. If more rain has fallen than will fit into the measuring glass, measure the water in two or more smaller quantities and add them together to get the total rainfall ■

Gerald L. Shak

Layers of Forest Life

■At first glance, a forest may seem like a jumble of bushes and trees. Look around in a woods though, and you will begin to see a pattern— the plants are arranged in layers.

High above your head, the canopy is warmer, sunnier, and windier than the layers below it. At your feet, the herb layer is dim and cool, with moist, "muggy" air. In ways like these, each layer is a little different from the others. Because of these differences, each layer is the home of different kinds of animals.

Some kinds of animals are born, live, and die in just one layer of the forest. Some may catch their food in one layer and make their nests or dens in another. Others, such as squirrels and blue jays, may be found in all of the different layers. You'll find the greatest variety of life in the herb and forest-floor layers. Most forest insects, for example, spend part of their lives in or below the forest floor.

The drawing on the next page shows some of the animals you might find in the layers of an oak-hickory forest (a common kind of forest in central and eastern United States). No matter what kind of forest grows in your area, watch for the different layers of life on your next walk in the woods ■

Laurence P. Pringle

CRESTED FLY-CATCHER nests in holes in trees; feeds on insects in the canopy.

SCARLET TANAGER nests and feeds in the canopy, where it catches leaf-eating insects.

GRAY SQUIRREL nests in tree holes or builds leafy nests in the canopy; gathers food from all layers of the forest but especially from the forest floor.

WHITE-BREASTED NUTHATCH nests in holes in trees; feeds on insects found on the bark of trees in the canopy and understory.

CANOPY
The leafy crowns of the tallest trees make up the canopy. It may be anywhere from 25 to 250 feet high depending on the kind of trees and their age.

UNDERSTORY
The understory is made of young trees and trees that grow to be only about 20 feet high.

WOOD THRUSH nests in the shrub or understory layer; catches most of its insect food in the herb and forest floor layers.

GRAY FOX can climb trees and sometimes has its den in a hollow tree; eats mice, chipmunks, insects, berries from the herb and forest floor layers.

CHIPMUNK nests below the forest floor (and hibernates there in winter); sometimes climbs trees, but gathers seeds, berries, and small animal food mostly from the herb and forest floor layers.

AMERICAN TOAD lives on the forest floor, catching insects and snails, burrowing underground to hibernate in winter.

OVENBIRD nests on the forest floor; feeds there and in the herb layer.

BOX TURTLE eats insects, earthworms, and berries from the herb and forest floor layers, and digs underground in winter.

SHRUB LAYER
In some kinds of forests, especially dense evergreen forests, there may be so little light that no shrubs or bushes can grow.

HERB LAYER
The herb layer is made up of wildflowers, ferns, mushrooms, mosses, and other small plants.

FOREST FLOOR
On the forest floor, leaves and other plant and animal matter slowly decay and become soil.

Life in a Rotting Log

■Take a piece of crumbly, punky wood from a rotting log in your hands. Break it open. Break it again and again. You will discover that a dead log is far from dead. With all the living things found in a dead log—with their creeping and crawling, scurrying and scratching—you'll wonder why the log doesn't crawl away.

But the only movement a dead log makes is downward as it slowly "melts" into the forest litter and becomes part of the soil from which it grew. The life you find in, around, on, and under a dead log all help in the log's destruction. From the time a tree falls to the ground, thousands of plants and animals use it as home.

Living trees are full of animal homes—in knotholes, dead limbs, and under the bark. Whether it has fallen or is standing, a dead tree is host to a variety of life. The kinds of living things you find in a log depends on where the tree grew, the climate of the area, and the season during which you find the log. It also depends on how long the tree has been dead and the kind of tree it was.

An important point to remember is that all kinds of life—lichens, mushrooms, tree seedlings, sow bugs, carpenter ants, centipedes, deer mice— do not rush all at once to live in a fallen log. Nature is more orderly than that. There are waves of inhabitants, and each wave paves the way for the next group. This change is not sudden or easy to see. Each new wave

Have a jar, can, or some pill bottles along so that you can collect
some of the small animals you may find in a rotting log.

begins to move into a log long before the other plants and animals disappear completely.

Log exploring is fun, just as bird watching, rock collecting, or going to a zoo is fun. You can nearly always count on seeing something new and different.

A lot of the time you will be down on your hands and knees, so wear old clothes. The top layer of forest soil—called *humus*—is often a rich black color. This is not the usual kind of dirt, however, and it feels good in your hands. It even smells good. Humus is made up of tiny particles of decayed leaves, roots, bark, and other plant material.

Take along a shovel or trowel to loosen chunks of wood. I find that a garden cultivator (a clawlike hand tool) helps in scratching my way through a log. You should have a can or jar and some plastic pill bottles along to collect specimens. Later you will want to identify them. Bring a notebook and pencil to keep a record of your findings.

If a log is hollow, I try to see what animals have been living inside. There you will often find mammals, or signs of them. These animals will usually dash away quickly when you start examining the log. You may see chipmunks, red squirrels, a rabbit, or any of several kinds of mice. Watch out for snakes if you live in an area where poisonous kinds live. Snakes often hunt in logs for food because there are so many living things

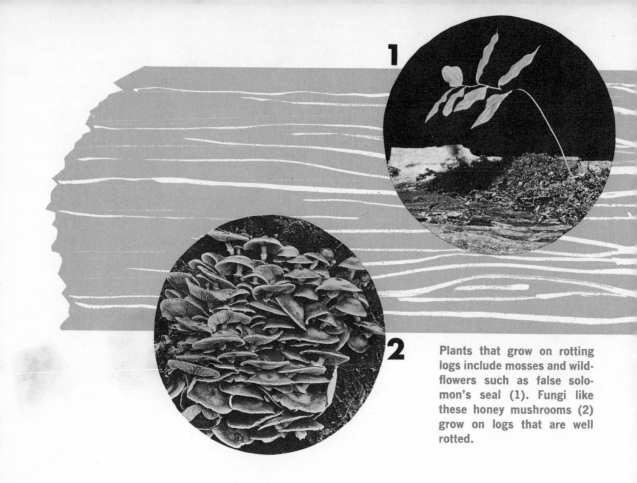

Plants that grow on rotting logs include mosses and wildflowers such as false solomon's seal (1). Fungi like these honey mushrooms (2) grow on logs that are well rotted.

in dead logs. Logs also offer shelter to these shy reptiles. I have found snakes in, on top of, and under logs. Sooner or later you will add snakes to your list of animals from rotting logs. Most of them will not be dangerous—but be careful.

Layers of Life in a Log

Once I have rattled a log, kicked it, and poked sticks into its hollow (if it has one), I start a closer examination, beginning on the outside. Mosses and fungi grow on a log's surface, except in very dry climates. You may find several kinds of each. Certain kinds of mushrooms will not grow on a newly fallen tree. The pioneers will be *sugar fungi* which prepare the way for others to follow. Not until a tough substance in the wood cells —called *lignin*—has begun to decay do the mushrooms appear. They are among the last fungi to grow on a rotting log.

Primitive plants such as mosses and fungi are not the only ones you will find. If the decaying log receives summer sunlight, seedlings will grow on it. In some forests you may find a few trees growing in straight lines. They may have all started growing on a rotting log.

You will probably find some insects on the log's surface, but more will be found in the darkness of the log itself. You may also find amphibians at or near the surface—a toad by the side of the log, or a salamander under

70

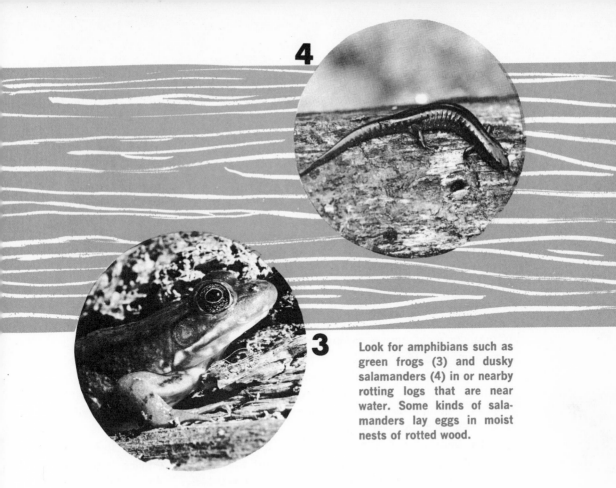

4

3

Look for amphibians such as green frogs (3) and dusky salamanders (4) in or nearby rotting logs that are near water. Some kinds of salamanders lay eggs in moist nests of rotted wood.

a scrap of bark (especially if the site is damp).

Now strip away a slab of rotten bark. If the bark is all gone, remove the first layer of loose wood. Here you are likely to find sow bugs, members of the *Crustacea* class of animals. Sow bugs are related to crayfish and crabs. You also may find spiders, representing the class *Arachnida;* millipedes (with a "thousand" legs) from the class *Diplopoda;* centipedes (with a "hundred" legs) from a class called *Chilopoda;* and beetles, representing the class *Insecta*. Where else could you find such fertile hunting grounds— five classes of animals represented in the first layer of a rotting log!

Many kinds of insects live in logs. Beetles and ants will probably be the most common. Also look for crickets, termites, cockroaches, and—in hollow logs—wasps and bees. If you do not find the adult forms of these insects, you may find their eggs or larvae.

If the log has decayed and you can dig through it easily, you may find plant growth all through it. In some places you will see masses of roots. Plants begin to use a rotting log for minerals and support even before the log has become part of the forest soil. From some logs you will be able to tear handfuls of ropy or stringlike material. This is the *cellulose* that makes up most of a plant's cell walls and remains after the lignin has decayed.

As you dig your way toward the middle of a hollow log, you will discover signs of mammals or reptiles that left earlier. You may see the dry, leaf

71

nests of chipmunks, or maybe the shed skin or white oblong eggs of a black snake. Once I discovered a nest of finely shredded inner bark. In it were four young flying squirrels.

Where the Log Meets the Soil

A log decays inside as well as outside. Rain comes in through holes, and the leaves, nuts, and acorns stored by animals decay. The rotting of the log goes on.

Eventually, you will come to the point where the log touches the soil, but the trick is to find this point. There is no clear-cut surface of either soil or log, unless the dead tree has just fallen. The log begins to merge with the soil. The rotting action of a log usually works fastest from the ground up. Moisture in the soil helps the growth of the bacteria and fungi that bring about decay. When you reach the soil, look for other animals and signs of them—a mole tunnel, earthworms, mites, and springtails. The soil is also teeming with life!

There is a long period between the time a tree dies and the time it is buried. This gives you a chance to watch the process, and to make lists of plants and animals you find taking part. Try scraping, chopping, and scratching your way through a log or two.

By looking at fresh logs, logs rotted to the soft stage, and logs that are little more than humps of earth, you will see that a fallen tree is a miniature "community." Since each rotting log is "alive," do not tear apart all of the logs in one area. Leave some, especially hollow logs, alone.

The tempo of life in a log follows the change of the seasons. Autumn

The author found this nestful of young flying squirrels in a rotting log. The squirrels were nearly full-grown and probably left the nest a few days after he put them back.

Beetles (1) are just one of many kinds of insects you may find in a rotting log. Centipedes (2) are attracted to logs because they feed on insects and lay their eggs in the moist wood. Deer mice (3) sleep in a log nest by day and prowl the forest floor at night. Besides seeds and insects, deer mice feed on land snails (4), which also live on or near rotting logs.

is an especially interesting time to search in rotting wood. As winter approaches, the plant and animal inhabitants get ready for the cold and deadly period ahead. You may find cocoons of certain butterflies and moths in cracks and crevices. Spiders often spin a protective web and fold up in a tiny nest.

A number of insects spend the winter in colonies. Masses of ants gather in rotting wood where they are insulated from freezing temperatures. Bees also will be inactive, or *dormant,* in their nests.

Snakes often spend the winter in logs. Some kinds gather and hibernate in groups. Squirrels and chipmunks use logs for storing nuts and acorns. You may find such a cache. With the coming of autumn and winter, life in a log slows down—but it never stops ■

Rod Cochran

73

Face to Face with Wild Mice

■Who lives in your garden, in the empty lot down the street, in the nearby forest or park? You have probably seen birds and squirrels in these places. You may have even noticed various insects, earthworms, and an occasional toad or snake. But how often do you see a small mammal—a mouse, mole, or shrew?

Maybe there aren't any small mammals living near you. Or maybe you just haven't been able to see them.

A good way to find out if there are any small mammals living nearby is to do some "live trapping." "Live traps" are traps especially designed to catch small mammals without hurting them. They are often used by biologists who want to find out what kinds of mammals and how many mammals live in a certain place.

You can buy live traps from some hardware stores. It is possible, however, for you to make your own inexpensive live traps for catching small mammals. The drawings on pages 76 and 77 show how to do it. Most of the materials you'll need are probably lying around your house right now.

Baiting and Setting

When you have made a few traps, decide what to use for bait. Many biologists use peanut butter. It is a messy business, but I mix dry oatmeal

74

with peanut butter. Use lots of oatmeal and only just enough peanut butter so that it all sticks together in little balls. Stick the bait on the end of the trigger just before setting the trap. Sometimes a little water makes the bait stick on better.

Set your traps in places where mice and other small mammals might live. For example, look for runways or tunnels in tall grass at the edge of fields, in marshy places, or under rotten leaves. Also watch for small holes in the ground. Alongside flat rocks and fallen trees in the woods are other good places to set traps.

When you place your trap, be sure that there is nothing to get in the way of the door when it closes. Set your trap without baiting it. Then tap it to see how easily it goes off. You may need to experiment with the setting to get the best sensitivity. Then bait and set. It is sometimes helpful to partly cover the trap with grass or leaves; this is to keep dogs, birds, and younger brothers and sisters from discovering the trap.

CAUTION!

Do not leave your trap set overnight in cold weather. You might freeze your catch. Traps should not be left set anytime unless you will be able to check them within four to eight hours. Some small mammals are not able to live longer than this without food.

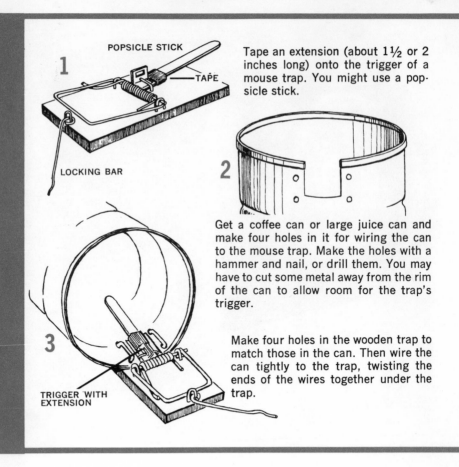

1 POPSICLE STICK — TAPE

LOCKING BAR

Tape an extension (about 1½ or 2 inches long) onto the trigger of a mouse trap. You might use a popsicle stick.

2

Get a coffee can or large juice can and make four holes in it for wiring the can to the mouse trap. Make the holes with a hammer and nail, or drill them. You may have to cut some metal away from the rim of the can to allow room for the trap's trigger.

3 TRIGGER WITH EXTENSION

Make four holes in the wooden trap to match those in the can. Then wire the can tightly to the trap, twisting the ends of the wires together under the trap.

When You Catch Something

Naturally, you should expect that the mammals you catch will be small enough to fit in your trap. Mammals of this size include deer mice, meadow mice (voles), jumping mice, shrews, chipmunks, rats, and, perhaps, moles. Some books that will help you to identify your catch are listed on page 122. Positive identification is not as easy as it seems.

Handling your catch can be a little difficult. I have lost more animals in my house than I have caught in it, so it is best to work outdoors. *You should think of the mice and other mammals you catch as dangerous beasts.* They can bite, though some species are much less likely to bite than others.

Suppose you have caught a deer mouse. The photos on pages 78-79 show how to handle it. *Be sure to wear gloves.* Remember that the mouse will wiggle and try to get away, so be on guard. Be careful not to hurt the mouse by pulling or pinching too hard. And remember, it takes practice.

If you want to keep an animal for several hours, a large, dry aquarium with a screened top is excellent for observing your catch. Be sure that the animal has plenty of food (such as grain or sunflower seeds) and water.

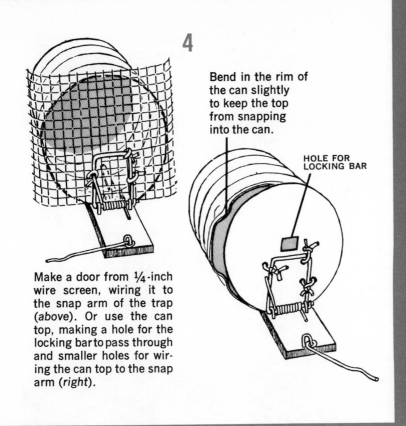

4

Bend in the rim of the can slightly to keep the top from snapping into the can.

HOLE FOR LOCKING BAR

Make a door from ¼-inch wire screen, wiring it to the snap arm of the trap (*above*). Or use the can top, making a hole for the locking bar to pass through and smaller holes for wiring the can top to the snap arm (*right*).

Most kinds of wild mice will tame easily and often make good pets, but it is best to let your catches go free soon after you have caught them. (Let them go in the same place you caught them.) If you should get a bite, treat it as you would any animal bite and get a tetanus shot from your doctor.

Marking Small Mammals

Sometimes it is important to mark an animal you catch so you can recognize it if you recapture it. One good way to mark small mammals is to paint their feet with a dab of modelmaker's paint. The paint will wear off in a month or two, but this is all the time you'll need for most of your investigations. By using different colors and different combinations of colors, you can mark a great many animals so that you can identify them quickly.

You might start by painting a different foot yellow on each of four mice. Then you could switch to a different color. You can also use different combinations of feet and, finally, different combinations of colors. Whatever

77

system you use, be sure to keep notes on how each animal is marked.

Try to keep the animal from licking the wet paint and from breathing too much of the fumes. Keep the animal in a cardboard box with an open top until the paint dries. Before trying to mark any animals, be sure to read about handling small mammals (*see below*).

As you learn more about trapping small mammals, you may think of some investigations to try. You might try to discover the size of the home ranges of different small mammals.

How Big a Home?

To learn about the home ranges of mice and other small mammals, begin by picking an area that is the same throughout—all woods, for example. Then make a simple map of your area and divide it into a grid (*see page 80*). Take the map with you as you set the traps, putting a trap at the places where the corners of the grid's squares meet each

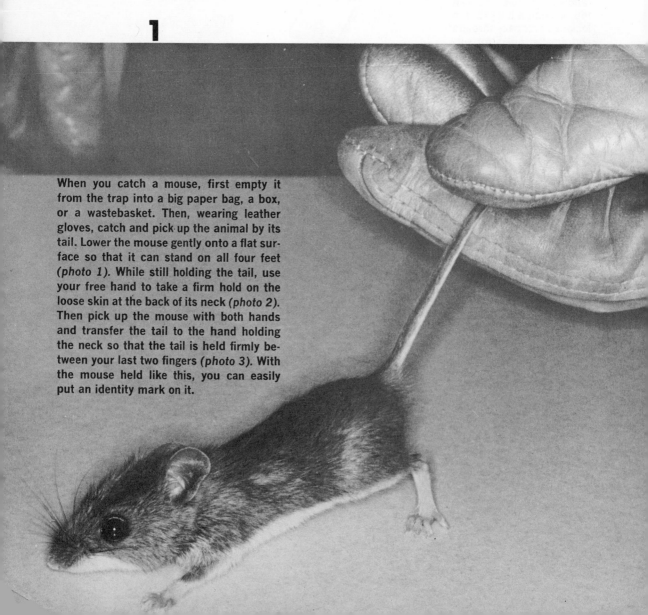

1

When you catch a mouse, first empty it from the trap into a big paper bag, a box, or a wastebasket. Then, wearing leather gloves, catch and pick up the animal by its tail. Lower the mouse gently onto a flat surface so that it can stand on all four feet (*photo 1*). While still holding the tail, use your free hand to take a firm hold on the loose skin at the back of its neck (*photo 2*). Then pick up the mouse with both hands and transfer the tail to the hand holding the neck so that the tail is held firmly between your last two fingers (*photo 3*). With the mouse held like this, you can easily put an identity mark on it.

other. You might begin by trying squares 50 feet by 50 feet or 100 feet by 100 feet.

A grid system is often used by biologists when they are trapping small mammals. If you put the traps anywhere you wanted to in your area, you might neglect some good places. The grid helps you prevent this kind of a mistake by having the traps spaced evenly over an area.

Set all the traps in the evening. Check them early the next morning. If you find an animal in one of your traps, mark it. Then make careful notes of (1) what you caught, (2) how you marked it, (3) date and time of day, and (4) where (on the map's grid) you caught the animal. A scientist would also be interested in the animal's measurements, sex, and weight.

Let the animal go in the same place that you caught it, and then rebait and reset your trap. You should check your traps again in the evening. Each day you do this, you will probably find that some animals will turn up in your traps again and again while others will have been caught for the first time. Eventually, you will catch most of the small mammals in the

2 **3**

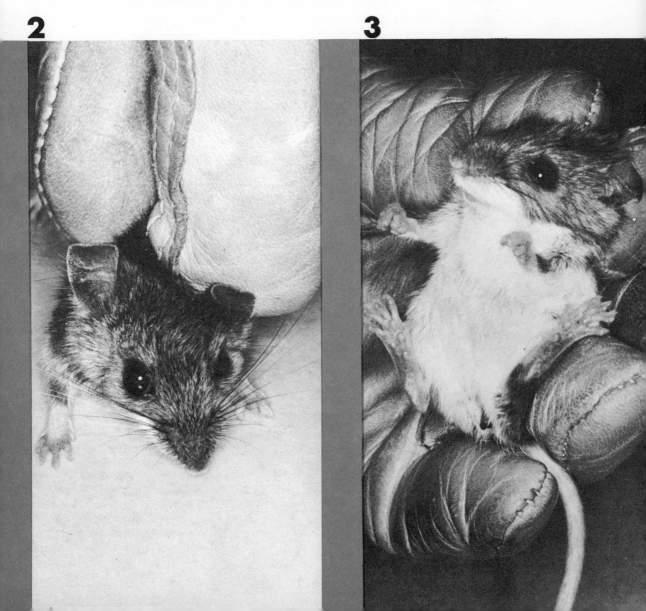

area. If you keep good records, you should be able to find out quite a lot about them.

Suppose you caught one mouse in several different traps. You could mark the positions of the traps on your map. By drawing lines that connect the different trap positions, you will get an idea of the home range of one mouse. You can try the same thing with other mice, and with other kinds of mammals.

More Puzzles to Solve

Biologists use live trapping to learn about the lives of small mammals. Once you start trapping these small creatures, you will want to make more traps. The more traps you have, the more you can discover about the small mammals in your area. You will probably find that your traps work best with mice. Moles and shrews are harder to catch alive, because they are less common and do not survive well in traps. Shrews, in particular, can live for only a few hours without food. If you catch a mole or shrew, let it go as soon as you can.

Here are some other questions you can try to answer after trapping an area for a couple of weeks:
- Which kind of animal did you catch most often?
- Which kind of animal did you catch least often?
- Did you catch more animals during the day or night?
- How many different kinds of animals did you catch?
- Did you have some animals that got caught again and again; others that may get caught only once? If so, can you figure out why?■

Christopher R. Hale

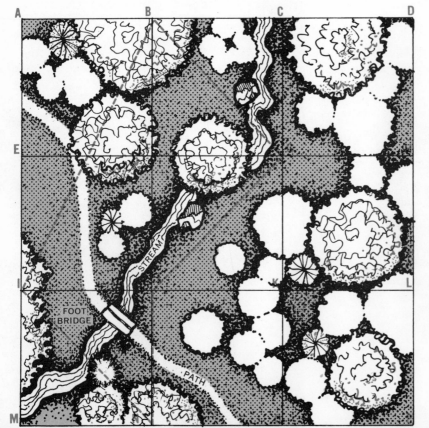

Make a map of the area you are going to trap, drawing in features like streams, paths, buildings, and fences. Then draw a grid on the map, marking the corners of the grid's squares with letters. The corners are 100 feet apart on the map shown here. Set a live trap at each corner and keep a record of where you catch certain mice. When you catch one mouse in several different traps, you can get an idea of the shape and size of its home range. For example, suppose a mouse was caught in traps B, I, N, J, and G. By drawing a line that connects all of these corners on the grid, you get a picture of the animal's home range.

Tales Told by Trees

■No matter how large or small a living tree is, it wraps a new layer of wood around itself each year—from the tip of its roots to its topmost twigs. If you cut across a root, tree trunk, or branch, these growth layers can be seen. They are called *annual rings*. One is added each year.

In most of the United States, trees grow their annual rings in two stages. Each ring has a light and a dark band, made of tiny parts called *cells*. The light band grows during the spring. Its cells grow quickly and have thin walls. The new cells produced during the summer grow more slowly and have thicker walls. Because of this, these bands are darker in color.

You may already know that you can tell the age of a tree by counting the annual rings on a stump or log. But annual rings are also records of events in a tree's past—a forest fire, an insect attack, a drought. Next time you come upon a sawed-off stump or log in the woods, see what the annual rings reveal.

As you look at a stump or the end of a log, the annual rings may not be the first thing you notice. If the tree is a large one, most likely there will be a dark section in the center surrounded by lighter wood. The darker part is called *heartwood,* and the wood around it, *sapwood*. The heartwood is the oldest wood in a tree. The cells of the heartwood have become clogged with gums, oils, and brown coloring substances (called *tannins*) which give the wood its dark color. If you look closely, you will see annual

81

rings in both the heartwood and sapwood.

Wide annual rings are formed when a tree grows rapidly. When a tree grows slowly, its annual rings are spaced close together. You may find the stump of a single tree that shows periods of rapid and slow growth (*see photo 1*). Look closely for annual rings with different widths. What do you suppose caused these differences? To figure out the causes, first think about the things that affect a tree's life—sunlight, water, and so on.

Into a Tree's Past

Some species of trees need more sunlight than others. Some grow well in the shade. Others, such as red pine, need a lot of sunlight. They grow slowly when shaded. If bigger trees are cut from around a red pine, giving it more sunlight, the pine will grow faster. Then its annual rings will be spaced farther apart.

Trees also compete for the water and minerals in the soil. Sometimes a few old trees slow the growth of many young trees because the old trees take so much of the water and minerals from the soil through their large root systems.

Insects can also affect tree growth. The pine sawfly, for instance, may eat many of the leaves of evergreen trees. Then the trees cannot make much food. They grow very little, leaving a narrow annual ring for that year (*see photo 2*). The gypsy moth can have the same effect on trees such as oaks and maples. Fire and disease also slow the growth of trees. You may find signs of past forest fires when you look at tree stumps (*see photo 3*).

If rainfall and snowfall drop below normal for a year or more, trees grow slowly. Since the oldest living things on earth are trees, the secrets held within their annual rings are of great interest to scientists. Some kinds of trees have been keeping records of the weather much longer than man has been keeping them, at least in North America. For example, some giant sequoias in California are over three thousand years old.

Some of the most dramatic annual-ring detective work has been done in the southwestern United States. By studying tree rings, scientists discovered that there was a bad drought from about the year 1276 to 1300. This long dry spell apparently caused the Indians to desert their cliff dwellings at Mesa Verde, Colorado.

In this case, a tree's history gave a clue to something that happened in human history. The tree stumps you find in the woods may also give some

82

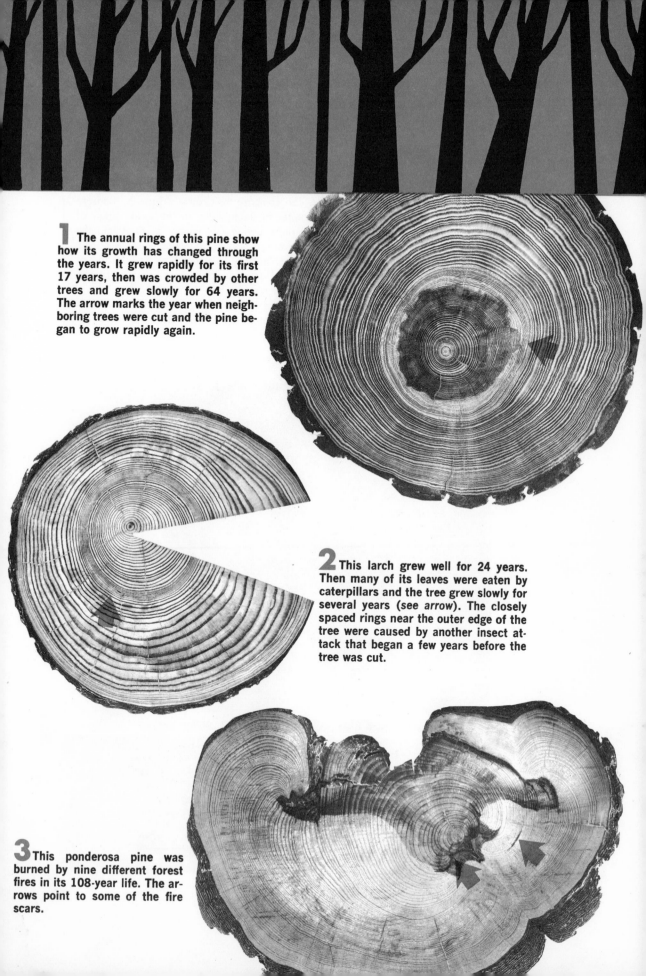

1 The annual rings of this pine show how its growth has changed through the years. It grew rapidly for its first 17 years, then was crowded by other trees and grew slowly for 64 years. The arrow marks the year when neighboring trees were cut and the pine began to grow rapidly again.

2 This larch grew well for 24 years. Then many of its leaves were eaten by caterpillars and the tree grew slowly for several years (*see arrow*). The closely spaced rings near the outer edge of the tree were caused by another insect attack that began a few years before the tree was cut.

3 This ponderosa pine was burned by nine different forest fires in its 108-year life. The arrows point to some of the fire scars.

clues to fires, droughts, and other happenings that affected both trees and humans. The pictures on these pages will help you figure out the tales told by tree rings■ *Rod Cochran*

PROJECT

Different kinds (*species*) of trees grow at different rates. If you have stumps or logs of two kinds of trees, you can compare their rates of growth. Measure in inches the distance from the center of each stump to the inside edge of its bark, then count the number of rings. Divide the number of rings into the number of inches and you get the *average* number of annual rings per inch.

You might find, for example, that a Douglas fir stump had an average of eleven rings to the inch, while a black locust stump had an average of five rings to the inch. Which tree grew at a faster rate?

Would this mean that the black locust tree grew only about one fifth of an inch thicker each year? (Remember that a tree grows outward in all directions from its center.)

Foresters use a device called an increment borer to see how fast a living tree is growing. As the borer is twisted into a tree, it cuts a rod-like core of wood. This core can then be pulled out and studied. The core shown above has close-spaced annual rings near the bark, a sign of slow growth in recent years.

How to be a Twig Detective

■Sometimes being a scientist is like being a detective. In both jobs, you may have only a few clues to help you solve a problem.

Imagine that you are a plant "detective." You are given a single clue: a twig from a tree. What can you discover about the twig?

To find out, you will need a twig. Cut one from a tree that has lost its leaves. Clip the twig off cleanly about six inches from its tip.

You will see all sorts of markings and bumps on your twig (*see page 86*). Depending on the type of tree, the twig may feel sticky, or hairy, or have thorns. Botanists can identify many trees just by looking at twigs. Later you might cut twigs from several kinds of trees and see how they differ.

All of the strange-looking bumps and markings on a twig are important to the life of a tree. Most of a tree's growth takes place in the twigs. Leaves grow from twigs, and twigs also produce flowers from which seeds, fruits, or nuts develop. Eventually, twigs grow into branches.

The odd-shaped bumps on twigs are called *buds*. Some buds produce leaves, while new twigs and flowers grow from other buds. Nearly all twigs have a large bud or group of buds at their tip—called a *terminal* bud— which is the source of the next year's twig growth. The smaller buds that stick out along the side of a twig usually grow into leaves or flowers. Some other buds along the twig usually do not develop at all. They grow only if the terminal bud or some leaf or flower buds are injured.

Buds are usually covered by overlapping scales that protect them from cold temperatures, injury, and insects. If you carefully peel away these scales, you will see some tightly-packed green tissue inside the bud. If left alone, this tissue will grow into next spring's leaves or flowers.

Reading the Past

Buds are important to the future of a tree, but you can also learn something about the past of a tree from its twigs. Look at the base of the buds on your twig. Below some buds you will see a scar which is the place where a leaf grew during the past summer.

When a leaf dies, a corky layer grows between the stem of the leaf and its twig. This corky layer—called a *leaf scar*—is left when the leaf falls off. How many leaf scars can you find on your twig?

If you look closely at a leaf scar (a magnifying glass will help), you will see some dots on its surface. These dots—called *bundle scars*—are the remains of tiny "pipelines" through which food and water flowed between the twig and the leaf. Count the number of bundle scars on several leaf scars of your twig. Did each leaf have the same number of "pipeline" holes?

Twigs have another type of scar, called a *bud* scar. These scars are rings of small, narrow marks left by bud scales when they fall away from the base of an opening bud. The most noticeable bud scars are left by the terminal buds. Each bud scar marks the place where a terminal bud began growing into a new section of twig. A twig gets one of these ringlike scars each year. How many of these scars can you find on your twig?

The distance between bud scars is the length that the twig grew in a particular year (*see diagram*). You can find out how much your twig grew

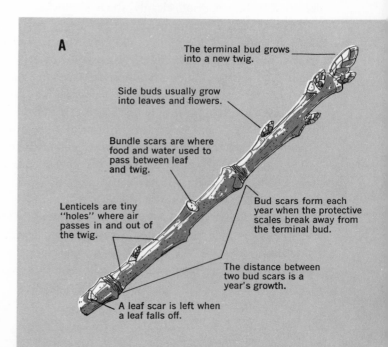

A

The terminal bud grows into a new twig.

Side buds usually grow into leaves and flowers.

Bundle scars are where food and water used to pass between leaf and twig.

Lenticels are tiny "holes" where air passes in and out of the twig.

Bud scars form each year when the protective scales break away from the terminal bud.

The distance between two bud scars is a year's growth.

A leaf scar is left when a leaf falls off.

86

in the past year by measuring the distance from the twig's tip to the nearest bud scar. (This new growth is often easy to see because its color is usually lighter than the older parts of a twig.)

Measure the distance between the other bud scars on your twig. Are they the same for each year? The growth of a twig varies from year to year, depending on the amount of sunlight, water, minerals, and gases it gets. Compare twigs from several places on the same tree. Did they all grow the same distance during the past year?

Besides buds and scars, you may see some small speckles scattered along your twig. These speckles are called *lenticels,* and air goes into and out of the twig through them. Lenticels are easy to see on some twigs—such as cherry and peach—because their light color stands out against the dark twig ■

Harold Hungerford

INVESTIGATIONS

You can bring certain kinds of twigs indoors in winter and "force" them to leaf out or to flower. (There has to be a period of four to six weeks with temperatures below 37° F. before forcing is successful.) First cut some twigs from several kinds of trees or shrubs. (To keep from injuring a plant, do not cut more than a couple of twigs from it.) Then put them in a vase or jar that is partly filled with water. Set the jar near a window, and then examine the twigs each day for a week or two.

Notice which buds open first. Are there any buds that do not open at all?

Cut two twigs from the same tree, remove the terminal bud from one, and then set them both in water. Notice the buds which open on each twig. Does the removal of the terminal bud have any effect on the rest of the buds?

Take another twig and cut a slit halfway around it, just above one of the side buds. This will stop the flow of some minerals and water from going up the twig beyond the bud. Then notice if this bud grows faster or slower than others.

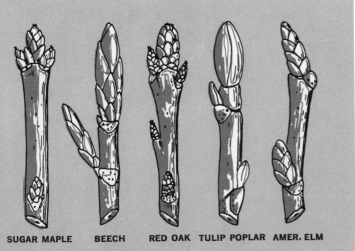

SUGAR MAPLE   BEECH   RED OAK   TULIP POPLAR   AMER. ELM

Many trees can be identified by their twigs. These drawings show how the twigs of five different kinds of trees differ in size, shape, and markings.

87

Exploring a Pond

How to Explore a Pond

■People have always been attracted to ponds, bogs, swamps, and marshes. No wonder—these quiet waters are the home of a wonderful variety of plants and animals. There are fish to catch, birds to watch, tadpoles and turtles to collect and raise.

The chances are there's a pond nearby that you can explore this summer. If there are no natural ponds, there are probably some man-made ones. As you explore the edge of a pond (or marsh, or swamp, or lake), remember that the many living things there make up a sort of community. You can try to discover how the different kinds of plants and animals fit into this community. You'll also find that these communities vary from pond to pond, and in different parts of the country.

Imagine that you are standing on a hill overlooking a pond. You are surrounded by trees—oaks, maples, beeches.

As you walk down the slope, mosquitoes may start to annoy you—they began their life in the pond. As you leave the trees behind and work your way among young willows and alder shrubs, your feet may sink into the mud. Ahead are sedges (marsh grasses) and cattails. Frogs sit on rocks or driftwood among the reeds . . . dragonflies dart about . . . a water snake glides through the mud.

In wading boots, you can push through the cattails to see the open water. Here and there it is dotted with water lilies. This is a good spot to stop and look around.

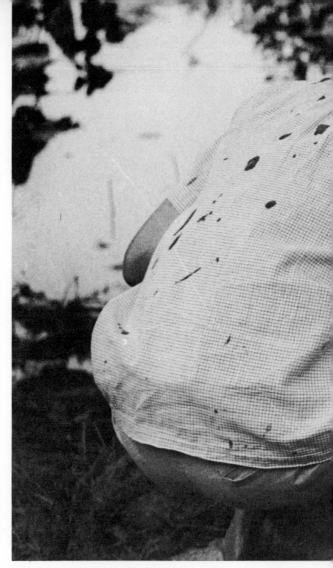

You can observe the small pond animals you catch by releasing them in a shallow pan. Put them back into the pond unless you are sure you can give them good care at home. The drawings on page 92 show some of the equipment you can use to catch and study pond animals.

Birth and Death of a Pond

A pond forms when water is trapped in a pocket of land and cannot drain away. Some ponds were formed thousands of years ago, when glaciers gouged out valleys across much of the northern United States. Other ponds begin when a river cuts a new course and leaves part of its old channel behind. Sometimes people make ponds by damming small streams or by digging out basins with a bulldozer.

No matter how a pond is made, it immediately starts to disappear. Scientists who study the history of the earth (called *geologists*) consider ponds to be temporary things—lasting just a few thousand years. That may seem long to us, but it is a short time compared with the age of the earth—perhaps 4½ billion years.

As soon as a pond forms, it begins to vanish. Soil washed in from the surrounding land begins to fill it. The dead bodies of tiny plants and animals

90

settle on the bottom. Plants begin to grow along the shore. When some of these plants die, their remains also settle to the bottom.

As the remains of plants and animals pile up on the bottom, the water becomes shallower and the shore plants grow out farther toward the center of the pond. Year by year the plants creep inward. Eventually, the pond is completely filled in. In much of the United States, the filled-in pond is covered by a forest if the area is undisturbed by humans. In the prairie states of the central United States, the pond becomes a grassland.

Case of the Disappearing Pond

As you explore a pond, look for clues that hint at its future disappearance. Is the pond bottom bare or is it covered with leaves and other parts of dead plants? Look for different "zones" of plants. You'll probably find at least four or five zones. One is made up of *floating* plants that have no contact with the bottom. There may also be *submerged* plants that grow on the bottom but do not reach the surface.

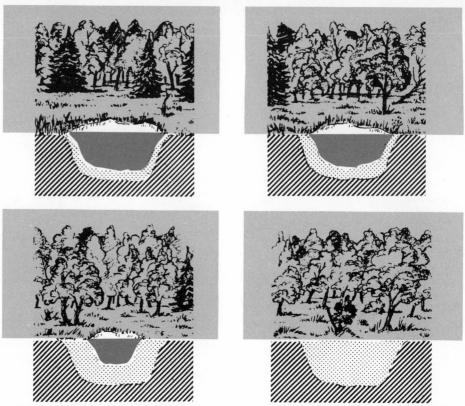

Ponds gradually disappear as they are filled in with soil and the remains of dead plants and animals. As the water gets shallower, the plants at the pond edge creep inward. After thousands of years, the pond is completely filled in.

EQUIPMENT FOR STUDYING POND ANIMALS

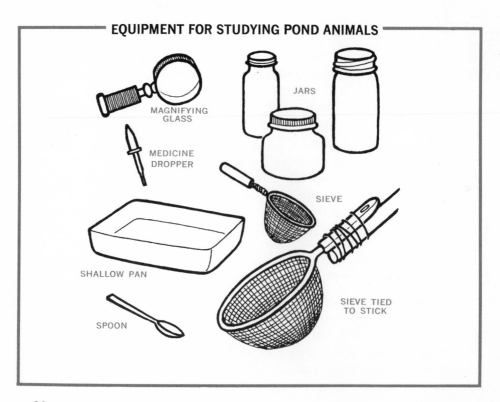

MAGNIFYING GLASS

MEDICINE DROPPER

SHALLOW PAN

SPOON

JARS

SIEVE

SIEVE TIED TO STICK

Closer to shore, you'll find *emergent* plants, rooted in the soil at the bottom of the pond but sticking out of the water. Emergent plants include cattails, bulrushes, and arrowheads. Next is a zone of plants that grow in the wet muck at the pond's edge. Beyond that, on drier ground, are shrubs and trees or grasses.

You may find one pond that has all of these zones of plant life and another pond with practically no plants along its shore. Which is younger? Do you think you could tell a natural pond from a man-made one by looking at the plants in and around it?

As you explore the edge of a pond, make a sketch of the plant zones you

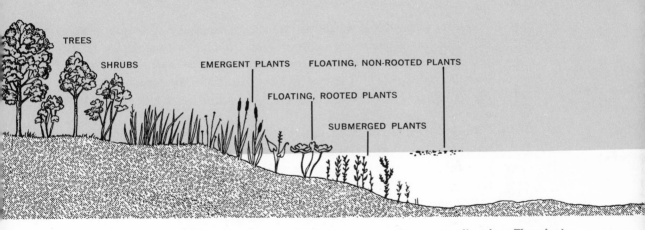

Notice the zones of plant life growing along a pond's edge. The plant zones and the kinds of plants in them vary from pond to pond. You'll find different kinds of animals living in each zone, too.

find. Your sketch might look like the diagram above . Then, as you visit the pond from time to time, make notes on where you find certain animals or their signs. Some animals, like muskrats, spend most of their time in the water. Spotted sandpipers may use only the zone right along the edge of the water. What about an animal like the raccoon? Where might it be found around a pond? Try to figure out why certain animals use particular areas and not others. Carry a notebook and keep a record of what you see.

Later in this chapter you can read about the snails, turtles, and insects that live in ponds. But these are just a few of the animals you can find and study.

The *mammals* that live around ponds are active mostly at night. They include muskrats, mink, and raccoons, as well as the more rare river otters and beavers. You may find their tracks in the mud. The shape of their feet offers some clues about the kind of life these animals lead. Is there webbing between the toes? How might this help an animal? Look for signs of the animals' feeding.

Muskrats are sometimes active during the day. You may see one swimming out in the pond or feeding on the shore. Try to find out how the animal's long, hairless tail is used for swimming. Also look for the animal's den. It may be a hut made of reeds and cattails, or a tunnel dug into the bank.

Ponds and other wet areas attract many birds. They range from tiny marsh wrens, building their nests among cattail stems, to four-foot-high great blue herons, prowling through the water for food. Watch to see what different kinds of birds eat, where they nest, and what parts of the pond they use.

Besides a pencil and notebook (and insect repellent), you may want to take some other equipment on your pond exploration trips. If you're particularly interested in birds, carry binoculars and a field guide (*see the book list on page 121*). The diagrams on page 92 show equipment you can use to collect water insects, tadpoles, salamanders, and other small water animals for study at home.

Visit a pond as often as you can. There's always something going on. Sit quietly and watch. You may see a kingfisher plunge into the water after a minnow, a frog snap up an insect with its long tongue, or a muskrat building its house for the winter. In any season, life around a pond is full of exciting events to see and mysteries to solve ■

Laurence P. Pringle

The Web of Pond Life

■Think of all the different people who live in your city or town. Some are milkmen, teachers, lawyers, or grocers. Others are students, housewives, or dentists. Each has a job in the community.

The same is true of the different kinds of plants and animals that live in a pond. They are part of a community too, and each has a job. Take green plants, for example. They are *food producers*. They combine energy from the sun with water and minerals from the soil and store this energy in the form of fats, sugars, and other foods. The stored energy in green plants is then passed on to *plant-eating animals*. Some plant eaters are so small that you can see them only with a microscope. Others may be large, like muskrats and beavers.

Some animals are *meat eaters*. They feed mostly on the plant eaters. They, in turn, are eaten by other meat eaters, and energy is passed from one to another.

When a plant or animal dies, some of its stored energy may be passed on to an animal that eats dead plants and animals. Or the dead plant or animal may slowly decay. Its energy is taken in by bacteria and molds as they break down the material in the dead organism into simpler substances. Some of the dead organism also becomes part of the soil, and later may be taken into the roots of a plant. Then the cycle of energy starts all over again. The drawing on the next two pages shows some of the complex web of pond life ■   *Laurence P. Pringle*

95

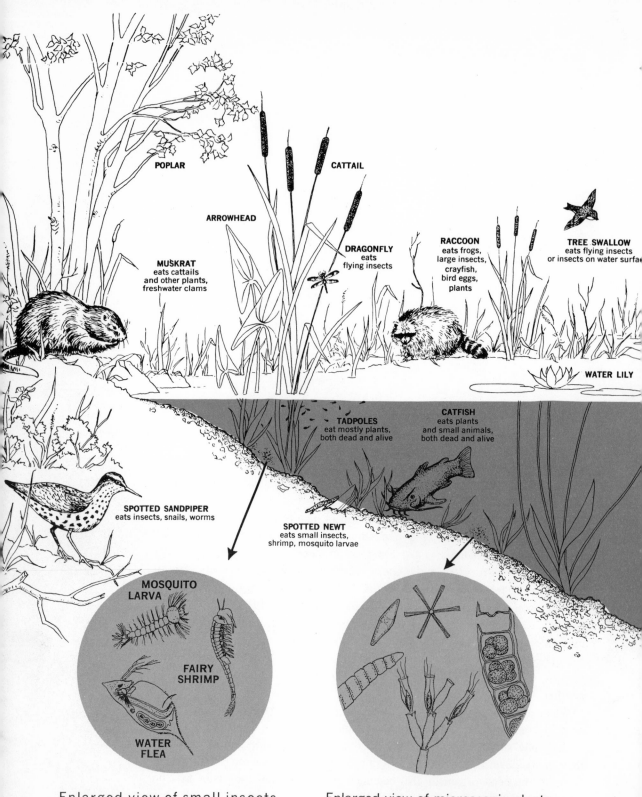

POPLAR

CATTAIL

ARROWHEAD

MUSKRAT
eats cattails
and other plants,
freshwater clams

DRAGONFLY
eats
flying insects

RACCOON
eats frogs,
large insects,
crayfish,
bird eggs,
plants

TREE SWALLOW
eats flying insects
or insects on water surface

WATER LILY

TADPOLES
eat mostly plants,
both dead and alive

CATFISH
eats plants
and small animals,
both dead and alive

SPOTTED SANDPIPER
eats insects, snails, worms

SPOTTED NEWT
eats small insects,
shrimp, mosquito larvae

**MOSQUITO
LARVA**

**FAIRY
SHRIMP**

**WATER
FLEA**

Enlarged view of small insects,
shrimp, and other animals that eat
microscopic plants and animals.
These animals are then eaten by big
insects, fish, and other meat-eaters.

Enlarged view of microscopic plants
and animals. The tiny plants, called
phytoplankton, use Sun energy to
make food and are the main source
of energy in a pond's web of life.

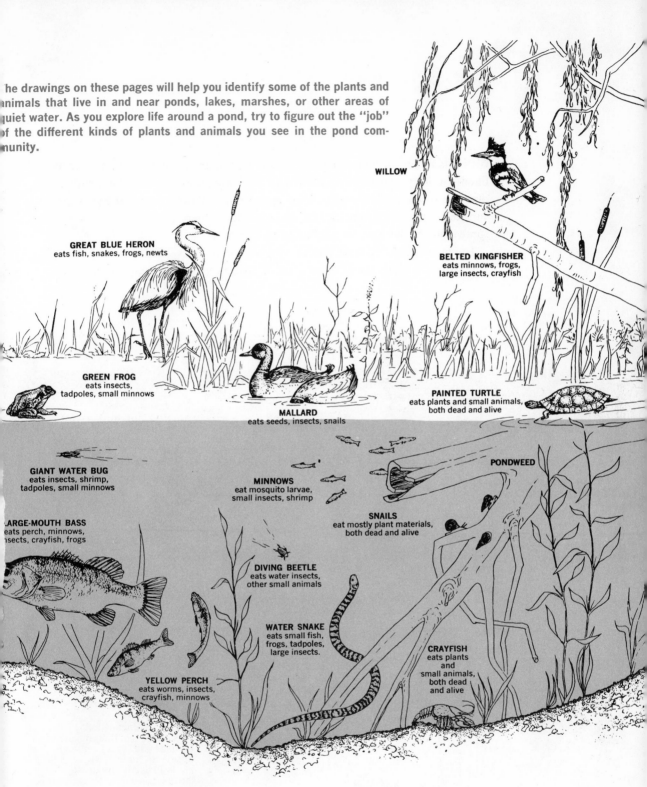

The drawings on these pages will help you identify some of the plants and animals that live in and near ponds, lakes, marshes, or other areas of quiet water. As you explore life around a pond, try to figure out the "job" of the different kinds of plants and animals you see in the pond community.

WILLOW

GREAT BLUE HERON
eats fish, snakes, frogs, newts

BELTED KINGFISHER
eats minnows, frogs, large insects, crayfish

GREEN FROG
eats insects, tadpoles, small minnows

MALLARD
eats seeds, insects, snails

PAINTED TURTLE
eats plants and small animals, both dead and alive

GIANT WATER BUG
eats insects, shrimp, tadpoles, small minnows

MINNOWS
eat mosquito larvae, small insects, shrimp

PONDWEED

SNAILS
eat mostly plant materials, both dead and alive

LARGE-MOUTH BASS
eats perch, minnows, insects, crayfish, frogs

DIVING BEETLE
eats water insects, other small animals

WATER SNAKE
eats small fish, frogs, tadpoles, large insects.

CRAYFISH
eats plants and small animals, both dead and alive

YELLOW PERCH
eats worms, insects, crayfish, minnows

97

Hunting Pond Insects

■It's lots of fun to hunt for pond insects and to try to find out how each is fitted for its particular way of living. You will often see insects "skating" over the surface of the water. Some spend most of their time just below the surface. Some climb among the water plants. Others swim in open water, sprawl on the bottom, or lie buried in the mud.

To catch and study these insects, you will need a sieve tied to a long stick; a wide-mouth quart jar of clear glass; a shallow pan of a light color, about

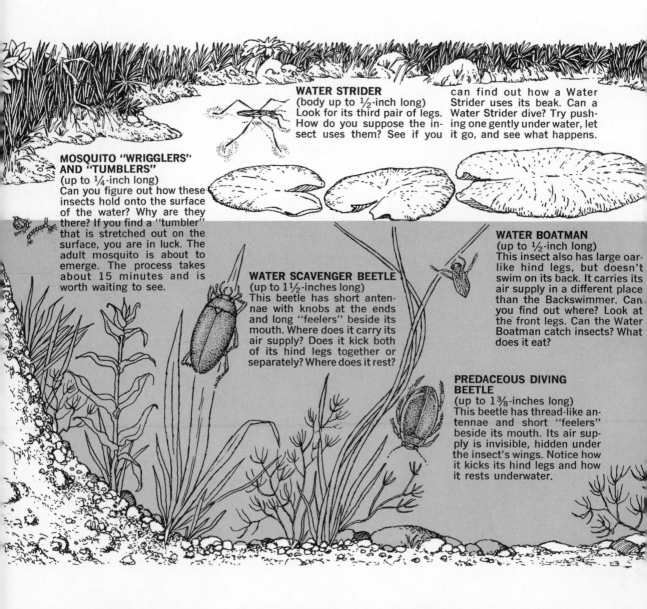

WATER STRIDER
(body up to ½-inch long)
Look for its third pair of legs. How do you suppose the insect uses them? See if you can find out how a Water Strider uses its beak. Can a Water Strider dive? Try pushing one gently under water, let it go, and see what happens.

MOSQUITO "WRIGGLERS" AND "TUMBLERS"
(up to ¼-inch long)
Can you figure out how these insects hold onto the surface of the water? Why are they there? If you find a "tumbler" that is stretched out on the surface, you are in luck. The adult mosquito is about to emerge. The process takes about 15 minutes and is worth waiting to see.

WATER SCAVENGER BEETLE
(up to 1½-inches long)
This beetle has short antennae with knobs at the ends and long "feelers" beside its mouth. Where does it carry its air supply? Does it kick both of its hind legs together or separately? Where does it rest?

WATER BOATMAN
(up to ½-inch long)
This insect also has large oar-like hind legs, but doesn't swim on its back. It carries its air supply in a different place than the Backswimmer. Can you find out where? Look at the front legs. Can the Water Boatman catch insects? What does it eat?

PREDACEOUS DIVING BEETLE
(up to 1⅜-inches long)
This beetle has thread-like antennae and short "feelers" beside its mouth. Its air supply is invisible, hidden under the insect's wings. Notice how it kicks its hind legs and how it rests underwater.

as big as a pie pan; a spoon; and a medicine dropper. A small pair of tweezers would be handy (not the eyebrow kind—they are too stiff). Take a magnifying glass, and a notebook so that you can keep a record of the things that you discover.

When you get to the pond, fill your jar about two thirds full of water. Put a little water into your pan, too. Now you are ready for any insect you may catch.

Catching Insects in Different Places

Probably the first kind you see will be shiny black oval ones about half an inch long, swimming rapidly in circles on the surface of the water. These are

WHIRLIGIG BEETLE
(up to ¾-inch long)
Look at the Whirligig's legs. Are they all alike? Are they all used in the same way? Try to find out how this beetle carries its air supply when it dives. Whirligigs have divided eyes. Would they need eyes like this if they lived under the water? Drop a small insect into the jar with the beetle. You may learn how a Whirligig eats.

GIANT WATER BUG
(up to 2½-inches long)
This bug uses its back two pairs of legs for rowing, and its front pair for seizing food. It can eat tadpoles and baby fish, so watch out for your fingers! Can you see where it carries its air supply and how it gets more air?

DRAGONFLY NYMPH
(up to 1½-inches long)
Put several of these in a jar together and see how their mouth parts work. Try to find out how these insects move about. You might try tickling one with a blade of grass to see how it moves when it is alarmed.

WATER SCORPION
(up to 3 inches long)
This bug looks like a twig. (It bites—watch out for your fingers!) It has trap-like front legs and a long breathing tube at the end of its body. How is the tube used to get air? Can the insect swim? Some kinds of Water Scorpions make a squeaking noise. Can you hear it? Drop another insect into the jar with one and see what happens.

BACKSWIMMER
(up to ½-inch long)
Although it can fly, the Backswimmer spends most of its life on its back, rowing through the water with its oarlike hind legs. Try to find out how it carries its air supply. Does the shape of its front legs give you a clue to what kind of food it eats?

whirligig beetles. Dip one out with your sieve and put it into your jar. Some things to look for and find out about this insect are listed with the drawing of a whirligig on page 99 . When you have studied one kind of insect, let it go and look for another kind.

Now skim the surface of the water quickly with your sieve. Rinse the sieve in your pan to wash out anything you have caught. Are there any very small insects that thrash about briefly, then float to the surface? These are probably the immature stages of mosquitoes. The long ones are *larvae,* or "wrigglers." The round ones are *pupae,* or "tumblers." Take up one of each with your medicine dropper or spoon, and put it in the jar, where you can look at it from the side with your magnifying glass.

In a spot where you look straight down into the water, you may see something swimming. Perhaps it is a water boatman or a back swimmer, a water scavenger or a predaceous diving beetle (*see diagrams, pages 98-99*). You can put any one of these into your jar to study it. *Be careful*—most of these big insects can bite. Also, they can escape by flying.

Some insects rest among the stems and leaves of water plants nearly all the time. Pull up a handful of water plants, put them in your pan, and see what you can find. Put a piece of plant into your jar, too, so that you can see how the insects climb.

To find insects that live in the pond bottom, scoop up a cupful of mud in your sieve and swish it back and forth in the water until most of the mud has washed through the screen. Dump what is left into your pan and watch closely until things start to move. (You might hurry up the process by draining off all the water.) Pick up the insects you want to see with tweezers or your dropper, and put them into the jar so you can look at them.

Many water insects are active at night. Try sealing a lighted flashlight and some stones for ballast into a big glass jar and sinking it in shallow water. The light will attract water insects as a porch light attracts moths.

You may be tempted to take home some big water insects and try to keep them in an aquarium. But most of them are cannibals. You can't keep more than one in a tank for very long, and it will need a steady supply of live insects for food. You can probably find out much more about water insects by watching them in the pond ∎

Alice Gray

Bring Them Back Alive

■To learn more about certain pond animals, you can collect them and study them at home for a time. Keep only the animals that you want to observe. When you put the animals in a pail or other container, be sure to keep the pail in the shade. If the water gets too warm, the animals will die. Also collect some pond plants—floating ones as well as rooted ones. The plants will provide shelter for the different kinds of animals in the pail, and keep them from eating each other until you can put them in separate containers.

1. Watch a Tadpole Change into a Frog (or Toad):

Place a tadpole in an enamel pan or plastic basin filled with three inches of water from the pond. In the pond, the tadpole feeds on algae (plants) such as *Spirogyra* and diatoms. At home, feed the tadpole one leaf each of raw spinach and lettuce. Do not feed it again until the leaves have been eaten. Change the water when it looks dirty, and only refill the pan with pond water or water from an aquarium. Gradually the tadpole will grow four legs. When it does, float a piece of wood in the pan so the tadpole will have something to crawl onto. At this stage the tadpole can jump around, so be sure to cover the pan with a piece of wire screen.

While watching and waiting for the changes to take place in the tadpole, record your observations in a notebook. Keeping records is an important part of scientific study. Well-kept records may help with the answers to

In the spring, female wood frogs lay eggs (*see below*) in woodland pools and the eggs are fertilized by the male frogs. The tiny tadpoles that hatch from the eggs grow quickly, usually having well-developed legs (*photo 1*) about two months later. Once the tadpoles transform into frogs (*photo 2*), the animals leave the water and live in the forest.

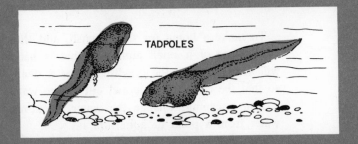

TADPOLES

Tadpoles are difficult to identify. One sure way to identify a tadpole is to feed it well, watch it transform into a frog, and then find the frog's name by looking in a field guide (see page 122).

many questions. Unless you have one of the small tadpoles that *transforms,* or changes, within a few weeks, you will also learn patience, for the tadpoles of the green frog and bullfrog take two, and sometimes three, summers to transform.

There will be changes going on inside the tadpole that you will not be able to see but may be able to think out for yourself. For example, when the tadpole transforms, it is no longer a plant eater but a meat eater. Changes must take place in its digestive system. You can read about the changes that take place inside the frog in books listed at the end of this book.

When the tadpole has transformed into a frog or toad, return it to the pond.

2. Watch a Crayfish Shed Its Shell:

Crayfishes are active at night and can be collected by flashlight. During the day they remain hidden under stones or in caves of their own making, and they have to be prodded out of their shelters with a stick.

One look at a crayfish will tell you it can nip. If you are quick, you can catch hold of the crayfish by the middle of the back, but it may be safer to use a dip net or strainer. Keep only one crayfish at a time. If you put two together they may fight.

---- QUESTIONS TO ANSWER ----

Before setting up a home for a crayfish, put it in a tank filled with water and observe it as it walks and swims about. How many legs can you find? How do they differ? Are some the same? How are they used? How does the animal eat? How does it walk and swim? What does it use its antennae for?

To make a home for the crayfish, add three inches of coarse gravel to the bottom of a small aquarium that is half-filled with pond water. You will soon see how the crayfish makes a den. Place a stone in the middle so that the crayfish can crawl out of the water. Cover the tank to prevent it from escaping. Change the water whenever it becomes dirty. Use only water from a pond or aquarium.

You can put water plants in the tank, but the crayfish may eat them. In the pond, the crayfish catches small fish, water insects, and other small animals for food. In captivity, the crayfish will take small pieces of fish and meat. When you feed the crayfish (two or three times a week) dangle the food in front of it with forceps (tweezers). Remove all uneaten food.

While you keep the crayfish under observation, you may be lucky and see it shed its shell. This hard outer shell is the animal's skeleton. It does not have a skeleton inside its body. Because the shell does not stretch,

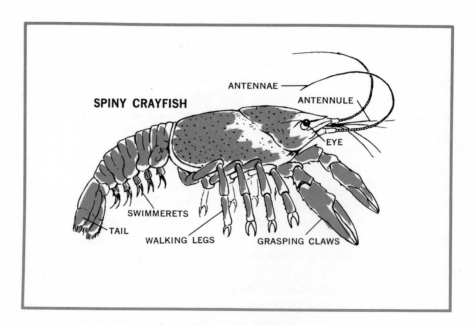

the crayfish must shed it in order to grow. The shell breaks open down the middle and the now soft-bodied crayfish pulls itself out. While its new skin is still elastic, the crayfish stretches as much as possible. In time the new skin hardens and after a while the crayfish sheds it again.

3. Study Some Salamanders:

Have you ever seen a salamander? Many people haven't because most salamanders stay under cover and are active only at night. They remain hidden under logs, rocks, or moss, or burrow down into the ground.

One common salamander is the red-spotted newt. It is active by day and lives in ponds, except during one stage of its life, when it lives on land and is called a "red eft." (In some parts of the country, such as Long Island, New York, there is no land stage.)

104

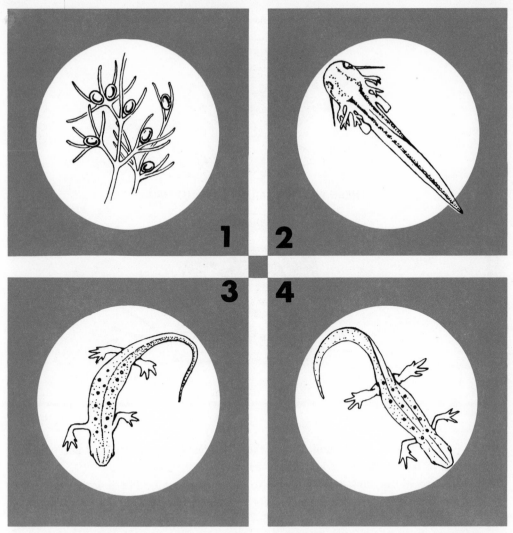

The female red-spotted newt lays her eggs singly on leaves of water plants (1). The larva, or young, (2) breathes through branching gills. By the end of summer it has lost its gills, grown lungs and legs, and is ready to live on land as "red eft" (3). After living on land from 1 to 3 years, the adult newt (4) returns to the water to mate and live for the rest of its life. (In some areas, there is no land stage.)

You can keep newts in an aquarium similar to the one for a crayfish. Newts are *carnivorous*—meat eaters. They will take pieces of fish and meat that you hold in forceps and wiggle in front of their heads. Feed them two or three times a week.

If you catch a newt and keep it in a tank, you may see it shed its skin. How does the animal do this? What happens to the skin?

4. Keep Some Pond Snails:

All pond snails are easy to keep, but tadpole snails are the most interesting because they are more active than other snails.

Look for pond snails on the underside of lily pads, on stems of other water plants, and under stones in the pond mud. Don't mistake land snails (which sometimes come to a pond's edge) for pond snails. To tell a land

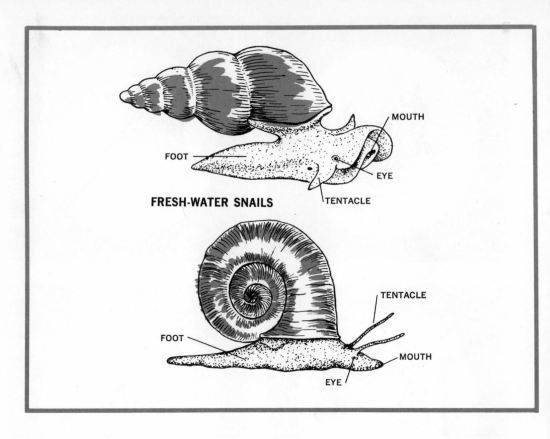

FOOT

MOUTH

EYE

TENTACLE

FRESH-WATER SNAILS

TENTACLE

FOOT

MOUTH

EYE

snail from a pond snail, count the tentacles on their heads. Land snails have four tentacles; water snails have two.

Use a fish tank or gallon jar to hold your snails. Put a layer of sand in the jar, plant some pond plants in it, and fill the jar with pond water. Your snails will feed on the plant stems and eat some of the algae that will grow in the jar. To be sure there is enough food, you can add a piece of lettuce once a week.

A few kinds of snails bear living young, but most lay eggs. In the pond, the eggs are usually laid on plants and stones. In an aquarium, snails

> ### THINGS TO WATCH FOR
>
> While observing the snails, see if you can find the answers to these questions: How does a snail move? Where are its eyes? Does it breathe by means of gills, as fishes do, or by a lung sac? (Gill-bearing snails have a horny plate called an "operculum" on the upper surface of the foot. When a snail pulls its foot into its shell, the operculum comes last and completely fills the opening of the shell. The body is then fully protected.) What is the snail's special eating tool?

often lay their eggs on the glass sides of the tank. If your snails do this, you will be able to watch the growing young snails through the clear jelly which surrounds the eggs. A hand lens or magnifying glass will help you to see the changes that take place ∎

Catherine M. Pessino

Frogs That "Sing" in the Spring

■Have you ever thought you heard sleigh bells tinkling on a warm spring night? It wasn't bells jingling, of course. You heard the "singing" of a chorus of male spring peepers.

Spring peepers are tree frogs. They are small, usually not more than an inch long. During the spring breeding season, male spring peepers "sing" to attract their mates. So do other kinds of frogs, but the peepers are usually first to call in spring. From a distance, they sound like bells.

You can find spring peepers in more than thirty eastern states. In western United States, you can find other tree frogs, such as the canyon tree frog and the Pacific tree frog. You can learn a lot about these fascinating frogs by spying on them. But first you have to find them.

Spying on Peepers

If you hear spring peepers calling nearby, look for them in wet areas such as water-filled ditches or small ponds near woods. Any of these places could conceal dozens of spring peepers.

Spring peepers sometimes call on cloudy, humid afternoons. However, the best time to spy on these tiny frogs is at night. For equipment, you will need a flashlight, a wrist watch with a second hand, a pencil, and a notebook. You will want to record what you see and hear.

107

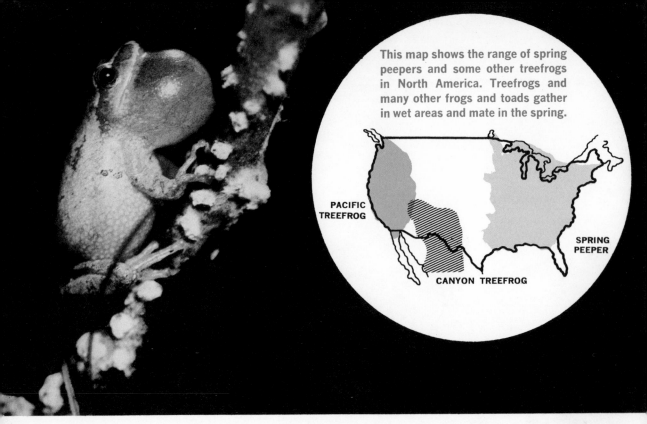

This map shows the range of spring peepers and some other treefrogs in North America. Treefrogs and many other frogs and toads gather in wet areas and mate in the spring.

PACIFIC TREEFROG

SPRING PEEPER

CANYON TREEFROG

Frogs, toads, and other amphibians must lay their eggs in wet places. In the spring, female peepers lay hundreds of eggs underwater.

Once you find a group of peepers, move very slowly and quietly. Try to creep close to them. Stop every minute or so and remain still. Listen carefully to the "singing." The sound you heard from a distance becomes a chorus of piping notes at close range. Each note starts sharply. It ends with a slight slur. It may sound like this: "Pe-rep."

Now try this: Shuffle your feet. Does the "singing" stop? Some scientists believe that frogs detect your presence by sensing vibrations from your movements through ground or water. The concert should resume in a short while if you remain still. Do all the peepers begin calling together? Write down what you hear.

Now look for the frogs. Sweep your flashlight beam over the area from which the loudest calling comes. Move the light along the water's edge. Watch clumps of branches or vegetation in the water.

The swollen *vocal sac* (*see photo above, left*) of the male spring peeper often gives away the frog's hiding place. The sac is a loose pouch of white skin on the frog's throat. The frog's call begins when air is brought up from its lungs, through the throat, and into the vocal sac. As air passes through the throat, it vibrates *vocal cords*. The quivering cords produce the sound. At the end of a call, the peeper's vocal sac is plump with air.

When you see a peeper in your light, keep him in the beam and observe closely. Does the frog seem disturbed by the light? Does he keep calling?

108

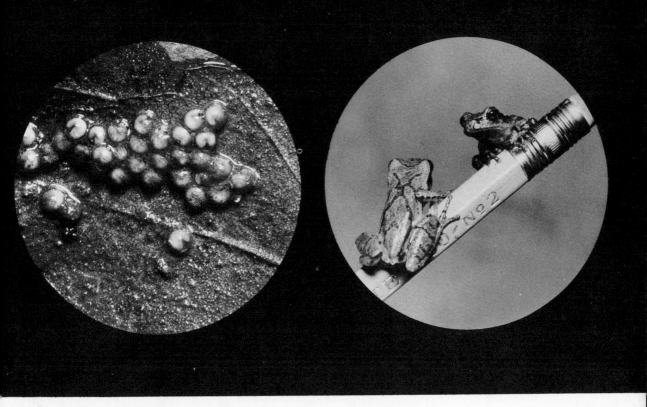

Tadpoles hatch from the eggs and gradually develop into tiny peepers like these that grow into inch-long adults.

The calling may attract a female. If you see two peepers close together in the water you probably have discovered a male and female mating. The female is larger.

Focus your attention on the call of one peeper. Use your watch to determine how many times the frog calls in a minute. How long is the interval between calls?

Catching and Keeping Peepers

Spring peepers live well in captivity. If you want to capture some to study at home, you will need a small net or kitchen strainer, and a wide-mouth jar or plastic container. Be sure that the jar or container has a top with holes in it that air can pass through. Put a wet cloth in the bottom of the jar. Peepers, and other frogs, absorb needed moisture through their skins.

Use the net or strainer to catch your frogs. Sometimes a fast—but gentle —hand will do just as well. You may collect more than one peeper at a time by sweeping a large, fine-mesh net through the water.

Have a home prepared for your catch. A five-gallon aquarium makes a fine one—it will hold four or five spring peepers. (You can also use a large mayonnaise jar, which is big enough for about two or three peepers.)

109

Spread a two-inch layer of coarse gravel on the aquarium bottom. Leave a clear area at one end of the tank, however. This will be the "pond."

Spread a half-inch layer of filter charcoal over the gravel (you can buy it from a pet shop). Then put some soil, moss, rocks, and twigs over this. Pour about two inches of water into the "pond" area. You now have a miniature pond and woodland for your frogs (*see below*).

Make sure that you place a screen over the top of the aquarium tank. Tree frogs are good climbers. You will understand why if you see a spring peeper climbing the side of your aquarium. Look at its feet. Notice the toes end in discs. How may this help the frog climb?

Most of the time, the peepers will stay on the floor of the aquarium. They need cool, damp quarters. Keep the aquarium out of strong light. Feed the peepers a few times a week on small mealworms or earthworms,

small spiders, and soft insects like flies. Frogs must have moving food or they will not eat readily. You might try feeding them hamburger by sticking a bit of it on the end of a thread and swinging it near them.

Captive spring peepers will call if not disturbed too often. Note the time of day and the room temperature when they call. Leave a thermometer in the aquarium where you can see it without disturbing the peepers. When are frogs most lively? Do they call only in the dark?

Free your spring peepers in the fall before the weather becomes too frosty. It is hard to get proper food for them in the winter unless you live in a place where it is warm all year around. Let your peepers go in the woods. They will spend the winter under the leaves.

Next spring your peepers and their fellows will awaken and head for water. The breeding season will begin and you will hear sleigh bells again on warm nights ∎

Edward R. Ricciuti

110

Plants That Eat Animals

■Many years ago, the few people who traveled to distant lands usually wrote books on their adventures so that stay-at-homes could share their experiences. In more than one of the books written about Australia and the island of Madagascar, a chapter was given to a story about "man-eating plants."

According to these books, the plants had long *tentacles,* or "feelers," that wrapped around a man just like the tentacles of an octopus. The screaming victim was carried into the mouthlike flower, swallowed, and digested. All that was left was a grinning skeleton. None of the travelers actually saw the plants, but they all said that they had been told about them by friends.

Today, we know that there are no man-eating plants. There are, however, plants that can eat insects such as mosquitoes and beetles, and other small animals. These are called *insectivorous* ("insect-eating"), or *carnivorous* ("meat-eating") plants. You can sometimes find these plants growing in swamps, bogs, and other wet areas.

Probably the best known of the insect-eating plants is the Venus's-flytrap. It grows in swamps in the Carolinas and a few other places. At the end of each of its leaves is a real trap, made of two flattened parts edged with curved teeth. If you look closely at the flat part, you will see that each surface has three thin hairs. The plant also has cells which make a

This housefly has landed on the lobed trap of a Venus's-flytrap. When it touches the trigger hairs of the trap, the two

chemical that attracts flying insects. When a fly lands on the trap, it touches the hairs. In some way that is not understood, the touching of the trigger hairs causes the trap to spring shut. Once the insect is trapped, its struggles cause the cells of the trap to produce a liquid. This liquid is made of chemicals called *enzymes,* which begin to digest the insect. The enzymes change the insect's body into liquids that the plant can soak up.

When most of the insect's body is digested (in a few days), the trap slowly opens. The insect's remains blow away in the breeze, and the trap is ready for its next victim.

Come into My Pitcher . . .

Another group of insect-eating plants is the *pitcher plants*. They are common in the northern United States and in Canada. Instead of trapping insects, pitcher plants let insects trap themselves. The pitcher-shaped leaves produce sugar nectars and odors that attract insects. When an insect lands

112

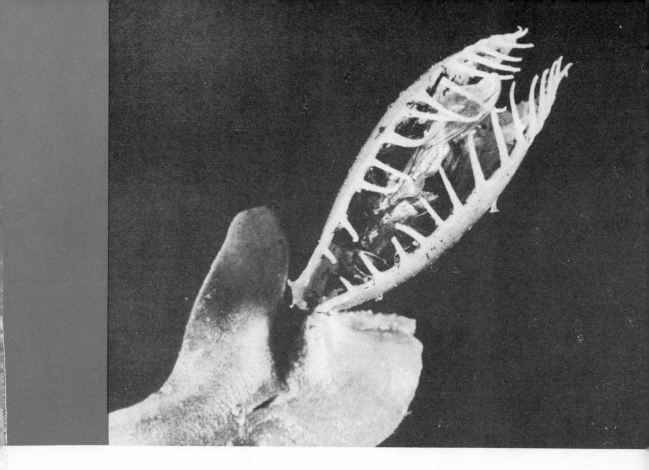

lobes snap together, enclosing the fly. After a few days the
fly's body is mostly digested and the traps open.

on the rim of the pitcher and tries to reach the nectar, it slips on the wax
coating of the rim and falls into the water-filled pit. Guard hairs, pointing
downward, keep the insect from crawling out. It drowns. Then its body
is slowly digested and the food is taken into the plant. If you cut open the
leaf of a pitcher plant, you can find the skeletons of flies, beetles, and
other insects.

Of all the insectivorous plants, the ones that are most interesting from
a scientific and engineering point of view are the *bladderworts*. These plants
live under the water. You can recognize them by their thin leaves and by
the small traps which grow on the side branches close to the main stem.
The trap, or bladder, is shaped differently in different kinds of bladderworts.
Usually, however, it is like a small sac, or bag, with a "mouth" or "door"
at one side. Many hairs surround the mouth. Some of these hairs act as
guides, bringing the insects close to the mouth. Others are "trigger hairs."

The trap is set when the mouth is closed and the sides of the sac
are pushed in. The water pressure is less inside than outside. When an insect

113

1 Insects that are lured into the pitcher-shaped leaves of pitcher plants drown inside and are slowly digested.

2 The traps of bladderworts catch insects and other small water animals that pass too close to the trap's mouth.

brushes a trigger hair, the mouth opens, and some water and the insect are sucked into the sac. As the insect is digested, some water passes out through the walls of the sac. This lowers the water pressure inside the sac, resetting the trap for its next capture.

The *sundews* are another group of common insect-eating plants. Their small leaves are flat at the tip and covered with small tentacles. These tentacles give out a sticky fluid. When insects land on a leaf, they stick to the fluid. The tentacles fold over the insect, and enzymes in the fluid begin to change the insect's body into food for the plant.

Some Unanswered Questions

As scientists learn more about these insectivorous plants, certain questions about them become more and more puzzling. We know, for example,

114

CUTAWAY VIEW OF A
PITCHER PLANT LEAF

GUARD "HAIRS"

INSECT REMAINS

2

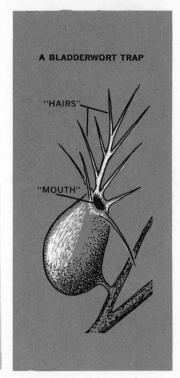

A BLADDERWORT TRAP

"HAIRS"

"MOUTH"

The trap of a Venus's-flytrap will not spring unless the insect touches two of the hairs, or touches one of the hairs twice quickly. You might try touching a single hair twice to spring the trap. Use a watch with a second hand and find out how quickly you must touch the trigger hair the second time to spring the trap.

You can feed small bits of meat, the white of a hard-boiled egg, or other food to a Venus's-flytrap. Will it digest paper or wood, or string?

● ● ●

RAISE YOUR OWN INSECT EATERS

There are five general types of insectivorous plants in the United States. All of them live in swamps or bogs, and most of them can be easily recognized. Many states have laws against collecting these rare plants. However, you can buy seeds of several kinds, particularly the Venus's-flytrap, from large seed companies. Biological supply companies, such as Turtox (8200 South Hoyne Ave., Chicago, Illinois 60620) or the Carolina Biological Supply Co. (Burlington, North Carolina) sell young plants or seeds of several different kinds of insectivorous plants. You can grow them in moist soil or in wet sphagnum moss. If the plants dry too rapidly, cover the pots with plastic bags, or grow them in a terrarium.

115

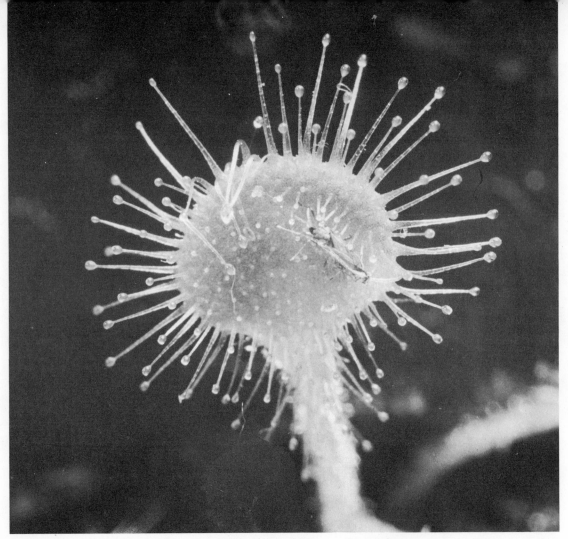

This closeup view shows an insect trapped on the sticky "hairs" of a sundew. Parts of the insect's body will slowly be changed into food that the plant can soak up.

that these plants are found in many parts of the world, and that they did not all develop from a single kind of plant. But we do not know when and where the different kinds of these plants first grew.

An even harder question to answer is this: How did these plants develop into insect eaters? They all grow in swamps or bogs, where the soil has few minerals that plants can use. Also, none of these plants have roots that are very good for taking minerals from the soil. Plants need minerals, especially those that contain *nitrogen,* in order to grow. Scientists have found that these plants will grow, flower, and form seeds without ever "tasting" an insect. But they grow better if they get nitrogen from the bodies of insects or if they are given the same amount of nitrogen in the form of fertilizer. This may explain *why* these plants developed into traps for insects. But exactly *how* this came about is a mystery that may never be solved ■

Richard M. Klein and Pamela C. Edsall

116

Trapped by a Turtle

■It all began in 1950, when Vivian Zeiller was just three years old. She was playing in the back yard of her home (in Tenafly, New Jersey) when a box turtle walked past. She tried to pick it up, the turtle snapped its lower shell shut, and Vivian's finger was caught.

Carrying the turtle, she ran to her father for help. He pried her finger loose. Vivian was free of the turtle, but her interest in turtles was just beginning. Her father built a cage for the turtle and Vivian began studying her new pet. But this was just the start.

Today the Zeiller turtle pen measures about thirty-five feet square. Inside are thirty box and wood turtles. Through the years, Vivian has marked each new turtle by filing V-shaped marks on the edge of its upper shell, or *carapace*. For example, Esmerelda, a female box turtle bought from a pet shop in 1963, has two file marks on the fifth plate from the rear on her left side. Her code number is L-5^2 (left side, fifth plate, two marks).

By keeping records like these, Vivian and her family hope to learn more about how long turtles live. Many turtles live at least fifteen or twenty years, but there is one record of a box turtle that lived 129 years. The Zeillers have already learned a lot about the lives of the turtles in their pen. Although box and wood turtles seldom go into the water, the pattern of their lives is like that of turtles you may find in ponds, marshes, and other wet areas.

Turtles Through the Seasons

In the fall, the turtles burrow into the leaves and soil, digging a hole that will be their winter home. (Pond turtles usually spend the winter in the mud at the pond bottom.) They reappear on warm days in late March or early April, and mate soon after leaving their winter dens.

In late June, the female digs a hole in the soft earth of a sunny area and lays her eggs, then covers them. The young hatch and crawl to the surface in the early fall, just a few weeks before they go underground for the winter.

If you want to catch some turtles to study, first check to find out what kinds are protected in your state. (To find out, call or write to the nearest office of your state conservation or fish and game department.) You can catch young pond turtles with a long-handled scoop net. Don't take more than you can easily care for. (For more information about turtles and their care, see the books listed on page 122)

Whether you keep your turtles in an outdoor pen or in an aquarium, they should have both land and water. In a pen, dig a hole in the ground, then set in a pan of water with its rim at ground level. In an aquarium, put in rocks which the turtles can crawl onto.

This young turtle has been marked by filing two V-shapes on the fifth plate from the rear on its left side. The turtle's code number would be L-5^2 (left side, fifth plate, two marks).

Many pet turtles die from lack of food, so be sure to feed yours well. The Zeillers feed each turtle a teaspoonful of canned dog food every three days. The turtles also eat melon rinds, peaches, other fruit, and tomatoes.

Weigh and measure your turtles from time to time. File a mark on a different part of each turtle's shell edge to tell them apart. (Never mark a turtle with paint—it may kill the animal.) Keep a record of the identity marks and measurements in a notebook.

See what you can find out about the lives of your turtles. How much time do different kinds of turtles spend in the water? How does a turtle swim? How are its feet used? Can it swim backward? Do your turtles seem to prefer certain kinds or colors of food?

Unless you plan to feed and care for your turtles indoors all winter long, you should let them go at the end of the summer. Release them in a woods or pond like the one where you found them. Someday you may return to that spot, catch a turtle, and recognize your mark on him. Then you can check your notebook and see how your old friend has grown through the years ■

Laurence P. Pringle

Young turtles hatch from eggs in the early fall and feed for a few weeks. Then they must dig underground to survive the cold of winter.

This photo compares a newly-hatched box turtle with an adult. If well-fed, a young turtle will double its size each year for several years.

Exploring in Books

■There are thousands of books available about the plants and animals of North America. The ones listed here are mostly field guides that will help you identify the life you discover outdoors. Also listed here are some books that suggest further nature explorations, and books that contain information that is usually lacking in field guides.

Several publishers have series of field guides or other books that are especially useful to a beginning "nature explorer." The Golden Nature Guide series is a valuable—and inexpensive—introduction to nature. The "Our Living World of Nature" series is beautifully illustrated and tells about the communities of plants and animals living in different North American habitats. Nature all over the world is described in the LIFE Nature Library. As first published, this series was most useful to adults and high school students; now simpler editions for younger readers are being published.

In the lists below, the simpler books are marked (I) for *Intermediate*. The more difficult books are marked (A) for *Advanced*. The first group includes miscellaneous subjects, but is mostly books about exploring nature; the other books are grouped by habitats or by kinds of living things■

Ecology, by Peter Farb, LIFE Nature Library, Time, Inc., 1963. (A)

Field Book of Nature Activities and Conservation, by William Hillcourt, G. P. Putnam's Sons, 1961. (I)

A Field Guide to Animal Tracks, by Olaus Murie, Houghton Mifflin Co., 1954. (A)

Fieldbook of Natural History, by E. Laurence Palmer, McGraw-Hill, 1949. (A)

The First Book of Animal Signs, by C. B. Colby, Franklin Watts, Inc., 1966. (I)

A Guide to Nature Projects, by Ted Pettit, W. W. Norton & Co., Inc., 1966. (I)

Reading the Landscape, by May T. Watts, Macmillan Co., 1964. (A)

Winter Science Activities, by John M. Youngpeter, Holiday House, 1966. (I)

FIELDS AND FORESTS

Birth of a Forest, by Millicent Selsam, Harper and Row, 1964. (I)

The Forest, by Peter Farb, LIFE Nature Library, Time, Inc., 1963. (A)

In Woods and Fields, by Margaret Buck, Abingdon Press, 1952. (I)

The Life of the Forest, Our Living World of Nature, by Jack McCormick, McGraw-Hill, 1966. (I)

PONDS AND STREAMS

Adventures with Freshwater Animals, by Richard Headstrom, J. B. Lippincott Co., 1964. (I)

The Fishes, by F. D. Ommanney, LIFE Nature Libary, Time, Inc., 1963. (A)

Fishes, A Golden Nature Guide, by Herbert Zim and Hurst Shoemaker, Golden Press, Inc., 1955. (I)

In Ponds and Streams, by Margaret Buck, Abingdon Press, 1955. (I)

The Life of Rivers and Streams, Our Living World of Nature, by Robert Usinger, McGraw-Hill, 1967. (I)

The Life of the Marsh, Our Living World of Nature, by William Niering, McGraw-Hill, 1967. (I)

The Life of the Pond, Our Living World of Nature, by William Amos, McGraw-Hill, 1967. (I)

The New Field Book of Freshwater Life, by Elsie Klots, G. P. Putnam's Sons, 1966. (A)

Pond Life, A Golden Nature Guide, by George Reid, Golden Press, Inc., 1967. (I)

The Tale of a Pond, by Henry Kane, Alfred A. Knopf, 1960. (I)

BIRDS

Audubon Land Bird Guide, 1949, **Audubon Water Bird Guide,** 1951, and **Audubon Western Bird Guide,** 1957, all by Richard Pough, Doubleday & Co., Inc. (A)

The Bird Watcher's Guide, by Henry Collins, Jr., Golden Press, Inc., 1961. (I)

The Birds, by Roger Tory Peterson, LIFE Nature Library, Time, Inc., 1963. (A)

Birds, A Golden Nature Guide, by Herbert Zim and Ira Gabrielson, Golden Press, Inc., 1961. (I)

Birds of North America, by C. Robbins, B. Bruun, and H. Zim, Golden Press, Inc., 1966. (A)

Field Guide to the Birds [eastern United States], 1947, **Field Guide to Western Birds,** 1961, by Roger Tory Peterson, Houghton Mifflin Co. (A)

A Guide to Bird Watching, by Joseph Hickey, Natural History Library, Doubleday & Co., Inc., 1963. (A)

MAMMALS

A Field Guide to the Mammals, by William Burt and Richard Grossenheider, Houghton Mifflin Co., 1964. (A)

The Mammal Guide, by Ralph Palmer, Doubleday & Co., Inc., 1954. (A)

The Mammals, by Richard Carrington, LIFE Nature Library, Time, Inc., 1963. (A)

Mammals, A Golden Nature Guide, by Herbert Zim and Donald Hoffmeister, Golden Press, Inc., 1955. (I)

Small Mammals are Where You Find Them, by Helen Tee Van, Alfred A. Knopf, 1966. (I)

REPTILES AND AMPHIBIANS

The Care of Pet Turtles, by H. G. Dowling and S. Spencook, New York Zoological Society, 1960. (I)

Field Book of Snakes, by K. P. Schmidt and D. D. Davis, G. P. Putnam's Sons, 1964. (A)

A Field Guide to Reptiles and Amphibians [eastern North America], by Roger Conant, 1958, and **A Field Guide to Western Reptiles and Amphibians,** by Robert C. Stebbins, 1966, Houghton Mifflin Co. (A)

The Reptiles, by Archie Carr, LIFE Nature Library, Time, Inc., 1963. (A)

Reptiles and Amphibians, A Golden Nature Guide, by Herbert Zim and Hobart Smith, Golden Press, Inc., 1956. (I)

Turtles, by R. Church, T. F. H. Publications, Inc., Jersey City, New Jersey, 1963. (I)

The World of the Frog and the Toad, by George Porter, J. B. Lippincott Co., 1967. (A)

INSECTS, SPIDERS, AND OTHER ANIMALS
WITHOUT BACKBONES

The Bug Club Book, by Gladys Conklin, Holiday House, 1966. (I)

Earthworms, by Dorothy Hogner, Thomas Y. Crowell Co., 1953. (I)

Field Book of Insects, by Frank Lutz, G. P. Putnam's Sons, 1948. (A)

The Insect Guide, by Ralph Swain, Doubleday & Co., Inc., 1948. (A)

The Insects, by Peter Farb, LIFE Nature Library, Time, Inc., 1962. (A)

Insects, A Golden Nature Guide, by Herbert Zim and Clarence Cottam, Golden Press, Inc., 1951. (I)

Spiders and How They Live, by Eugene David, Prentice-Hall, Inc., 1964. (I)

The Story of Spiders, by Dorothy Shuttlesworth, Doubleday & Co., Inc., 1959. (I)

PLANTS

Because of a Tree, by Lorus and Margery Milne, Atheneum Pubs., 1963. (I)

A Field Guide to Trees and Shrubs, by George Petrides, Houghton Mifflin Co., 1958. (A)

The First Book of Weeds, by Barbara Beck, Franklin Watts, Inc., 1963. (I)

Flowers, A Golden Nature Guide, by Herbert Zim and Alexander Martin, Golden Press, Inc., 1950. (I)

The New Field Book of American Wild Flowers, by Harold Rickett, G. P. Putnam's Sons, 1963. (A)

Non-Flowering Plants, A Golden Nature Guide, by Floyd Shuttleworth and Herbert Zim, Golden Press, Inc., 1967. (A)

The Plants, by Frits Went, LIFE Nature Library, Time, Inc., 1963. (A)

Trees, A Golden Nature Guide, by Herbert Zim and Alexander Martin, Golden Press, Inc., 1952. (I)

About Our Authors

Laurence P. Pringle grew up in the country near Rochester, New York. He studied wildlife conservation at Cornell University and at the University of Massachusetts. Presently he is *Executive Editor* of *Nature and Science* magazine, published at The American Museum of Natural History in New York City.

Margaret J. Anderson studied biology at Edinburgh University in Scotland and is now the wife of a professor at Oregon State University, Corvallis.

Kenneth Bobrowsky is Science Co-ordinator at the Bronx High School of Science in New York City. He has collected and studied reptiles in the southwestern United States and in Central America.

Rod Cochran is a wildlife biologist who is now in charge of publications at the New York State College of Forestry at Syracuse University.

Lawrence J. Crockett teaches courses in botany at the City College of New York, where he is Associate Professor in Biology.

Alice Gray is a Scientific Assistant in the Department of Entomology, The American Museum of Natural History.

Christopher R. Hale helps develop new ways of teaching science to young people at the Education Development Center in Newton, Massachusetts.

Florence Hoseney studies fungi and other plants at the University of Michigan, Ann Arbor.

Harold Hungerford teaches science at the University School, Southern Illinois University, Carbondale.

Richard M. Klein, formerly at the New York Botanical Garden is now Professor of Botany at the University of Vermont in Burlington. **Pamela C. Edsall** assisted his studies of plants at the New York Botanical Garden.

David Mech is a biologist and writer who has studied wolves at Isle Royale National Park and in his present home state, Minnesota.

Catherine M. Pessino is a Senior Instructor in the Education Department, The American Museum of Natural History.

Edward R. Ricciuti is editor of *Animal Kingdom* magazine, published by the New York Zoological Society at the Bronx Zoo.

Gerald L. Shak is User Services Representative of the United States Weather Bureau at Kennedy Airport, New York City.

Illustration Credits